The New Starting Right with Bees

A Beginner's Handbook on Beekeeping

21st Edition

Revised and Edited by the Editorial Staff of *Bee Culture* Magazine

- Kim Flottum
- Kathy Summers

Published by THE A.I. ROOT CO.
MEDINA, OHIO, U.S.A.

This book is the culmination of nearly 40 years work by the Editors and staff of *Gleanings In Bee Culture*. It's primary intent is as a learning tool for beginning beekeepers, but it is an exceptional source of information for anyone interested in the fascinating world of the honey bee.

This book covers every aspect of introductory beekeeping and honey bee biology — including seasonal management, equipment used, harvesting and marketing hive products, honey bee communication and beekeeping social skills.

Beekeeping can become a hobby, a part-time or full-time occupation, but whatever your eventual involvement, this book will make beekeeping easier — since you are "Starting Right With Bees".

Kim Flottum, Editor
Gleanings In Bee Culture
May, 1988

The New
Starting Right with Bees

Table of Contents

Preface iii

1. Suddenly You're a Beekeeper 1
2. Before You Start 7
3. Your First Inspection 21
4. Getting To Know Your Bees 32
5. Your First Honey Flow 40
6. Honey Plants and Pollination 48
7. Harvesting 53
8. Spring and Summer Management 65
9. Late Season Management 80
10. Packaging and Marketing Hive Products 88
11. Diseases and Pests of Honey Bees 101
12. Beekeeping Social Skills 113

   Epilog 122

   Glossary 123

   References 133

   Index 134

Introduction:
Who Can Keep Bees

Beekeeping is an activity for old or young, men or women. Even youngsters may keep bees for a 4-H or F.F.A. project, or to earn a Scout merit badge. Anybody with fair health and strength, who enjoys the outdoors, can become successful at beekeeping. City people can also keep bees in their back lots or on roof tops.

Not only are bees interesting themselves, but they are just one part of the natural world. They play an important role in the lives of plants who depend on their pollinating work. Many crops and flowers would not exist today without honey bees.

For the beginner, the best time to start bees is in the spring, during a fruit bloom. The reasons for starting early are twofold: there needs to be an ample supply of nectar and pollen for the bees to rear their brood, and they need to build up their population to survive over winter.

This book explains how to start a colony of bees, where to get the equipment, and what you need to do the first year. The books referred to in the reference section will give you a more complete understanding of the finer manipulations of experienced beekeepers, as well as explanations of what is going on inside the hive.

---

*Any new word used for the first time is shown in **bold**. A definition for it appears in the glossary.*

---

1. Suddenly You're A Beekeeper

Read This First

You are suddenly a beekeeper when your friends or relatives give you some bees, or a swarm of bees unexpectedly lands nearby. This chapter is just for these emergencies: how to hive a swarm, install a package or deal with a full hive of bees suddenly in your possession.

You are suddenly a beekeeper when a swarm of bees appears one day in your backyard. Don't Panic!

Equipment

While you should prepare your equipment several months before your bees arrive, you may suddenly find that you need a hive NOW. This will be the case if a **swarm*** has landed in your backyard (or in your neighbor's yard) and they need a home immediately. First Rule: DON'T PANIC! If a swarm has unexpectedly appeared that you want to keep, get on your **bee suit** and **veil**, and spray them with sugar syrup (in a 1:1 ratio sugar: hot water). Now find a sturdy box (cardboard or wood) that can be closed up, and put the bees in it. You can open the top of the box and lay the swarm inside or dislodge them so they fall inside.

If you cannot get a real **hive body** together in time, use this box as a temporary hive and set it up where you will be permanently locating it. Make sure the box has a small opening for the bees to come and go. Let this temporary hive alone until you have your hive equipment set up. Then transfer the bees there.

If you can do this in a day or two, merely shake the bees on the ground in front of your new hive. Do this in the late afternoon, and spray all the bees with warm sugar water to coat their wings and keep them from flying about.

If you cannot get to making bee equipment for a few days, confine the bees and place them in a dark place, like your garage. Make sure they will not get overheated and that they can

1

breathe. Covering the box with an old sheet or pillowcase is good. You may even consider feeding them.

This can be done by leaving a hole or crack at the top of the box. Make it about an inch in diameter. Then fill a quart jar with sugar syrup and punch a few small holes in the lid. Invert this over the hole so the bees have access to it and leave it alone until you are ready to hive it.

Sometimes calling local beekeepers will be helpful. They can sell you the equipment you need on the spot, and can offer some good advice on how to hive your swarm.

This is the basic equipment you will need:
- 1 wooden hive body (also called a brood chamber or deep super)
- 10 wooden frames
- 10 sheets of wired or plastic foundation
- 1 bottom board
- 1 inner cover
- 1 outer cover
- 1 smoker
- 1 veil
- 1 bee suit (optional)

Rules for Swarms and Packages

Whether you have a package or a swarm, you install them in a similar manner. Prepare your hive at its permanent location, if possible. (Once the bees have become established there, you may move them to a more appropriate location; see section on Moving Hives, this chapter). Make up some sugar syrup of 1:1 white sugar:hot water; never use honey or brown sugar for feeding bees liquid food.

• Swarms

If you have a SWARM, clip away all the extra branches, leaves, and twigs to expose the bees. Spray the swarm with syrup, coating their wings thoroughly, but do not soak the bees, especially if the weather is cool. You may have to spray them several times, as they clean themselves up. If you can, carefully detach the main branch(es) that hold the swarm. Be careful not to bump them, dislodging the bees. Now carry the swarm over and lay it in front of the new hive.

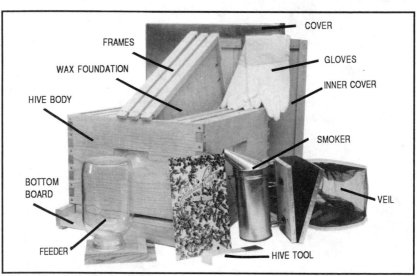

A beginner's beekeeping kit is available from most bee suppliers and should include these items.

They will march right in!

Once well sprayed with sugar syrup, a clustered swarm can be carefully cut away from it's original support, and carried to it's new home. G. A. Pauli, Photo.

If you cannot detach the swarm intact, you can shake them into a cardboard box, pillow case or other *breathable* container, and then carry that to your hive and shake them out. Some people place the new hive on top of a sheet so they can see the bees clearly (and even spot the queen) as the bees walk in. For a more complete discussion on swarms, please read Chapter 8.

• **Packages**

A **package** of bees is essentially a swarm in a screened container. Again, you will need your suit and veil, as well as a **hive tool**. Make up a batch of light 1:1 sugar syrup in a clean spray bottle. Before you install your bees, it is best to engorge them with syrup. You can do this by spray-ing the screen or by placing a feeder jar on the screen so the bees can feed themselves. Leave them until late afternoon.

A note on medicated syrup. Packages, and sometimes swarms, may be more susceptible to diseases during this stressful time. This is a good time to incorporate medicine in the syrup. Terramycin and fumagillin are the recommended drugs — these help control foulbrood and Nosema diseases. *Follow package directions when feeding TM-25 and fumagillin.*

Directions for Hiving your Package

1. If the weather is hot when the bees arrive, place the packages in a cool, dark room or garage. If the weather is cold, place them in a room not warmer than 70°F until they can be placed into the hive. (The weather is "hot" when it is warmer than 80°F and "cold" when it is cooler than 45°F.)
2. Each package contains a friction-top can of **sugar syrup**. During their trip, the bees feed on this syrup through the small holes. The queen is shipped in a special cage, suspended among the bees. It is called a **queen cage.**
3. Install your bees late in the afternoon if possible, to reduce **drifting.** Have the hives ready on permanent stands. At this point, just before shaking the bees out, spray them liberally with sugar syrup. Dampen the bees sufficiently so they become fairly inactive, but do NOT soak them.
4. Tap the cage on the ground so the bees fall to the bottom. Using the hive tool, pry up and remove the package cover board. Slowly remove the queen cage, which is usually suspended by a metal disk or a wire. You may have to

3

Pry up the cover over the feeder can and pull up on tab holding the queen cage. You may have to pull up on the feeder can to get the queen cage out.

remove feeder can first, then the queen cage. Re-cover the hole, shake off the clinging bees and examine the queen. She should be alive and active. Remove the cork in the end of the queen cage and replace with a piece of marshmallow. Slide the cage, plugged opening up, between the top bars of two middle frames; or lay the cage, wire side down, between 2 frames. The bees should be able to feed her through the wire. If the cage already has a **candy plug**, remove the cork covering it.

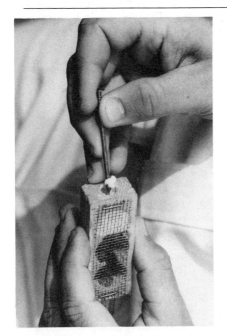

Before positioning the queen cage, punch a hole in the candy end with a nail. If there is a cork and no candy, remove the cork and substitute a piece of marshmallow.

Position the cage between two frames, candy side up, so the bees have access to the screen. Shake a cupful of bees over the cage, add the rest of the frames, and cover hive. Then shake remaining bees outside at the entrance.

5. Tap the package again to shake bees to the bottom. Remove the feeder can by tilting the bottom of the cage up a bit and letting the can slide out enough to grasp. Now shake a cupful of bees out through the opening on top of the queen cage.

6. Cover hive with inner cover. Shake the rest of the bees in front of the hive on the ground. (This lets all the dead bees fall outside the hive.) If the bees have been dampened with sugar syrup, there should be very few flying around. Watch the bees as they crawl in the entrance.

Place filled cans or jars of syrup over the hole in the inner cover. Protect them with an empty super, cover, and leave the bees alone for at least a week.

7. FEEDING. Feed warm sugar syrup using the feeder can in the shipping cage or other friction-top pails. Punch about a dozen holes in the lid of a jar with a small 3d nail. Plastic pail feeders with a mesh screen in place of holes are longer lasting, as they do not rust.

The feeder can filled with warm syrup is placed over the hole in the **inner cover** with the perforated lid down. If your hive does not have an inner cover, invert the pail of feed on the **top bars** of the **frames.** Put an empty **super** over the feeder can to protect it from rain or **robbing bees,** then place the outer cover on top.

8. Reduce the width of the hive entrance with grass or the **entrance reducer** to about one inch during feeding. DO NOT DISTURB THE BEES, OR LOOK FOR THE QUEEN FOR AT LEAST SEVEN DAYS. The only time the hive should be opened during this period is to refill an empty feeder. Continue feeding until **nectar** is plentiful (bees stop eating syrup). After a week, inspect the hive to see if the queen is laying; then remove the empty queen cage. If for any reason the queen has not been released from the cage, free her now by pulling open the screen.

Your curiosity to see "how the bees are doing" disturbs the bees unnecessarily. They will make greater headway if left for at least seven days without **any** disturbance.

NOTE: If the queen should arrive dead, notify dealer and unite bees with another package, using the **newspaper method** (see Chapter 9, Uniting Colonies).

9. If the bees arrive dead or in bad condition, have a claim made out at your Post Office and forward it to the shipper. A replacement will be mailed at once. Do not return the dead bees. The normal death rate of bees is high, so don't

be alarmed to find SOME dead bees on the package floor. However, if over an inch of dead bees is present, notify shipper.

Inspections

During the first inspection, seven days after the bees are installed, you should see eggs in the bottoms of the cells. A second inspection four or five days after that should reveal **capped larvae.**

If egg laying ceases, or has not started, locate the queen. Queen loss is not uncommon in colonies started from packages. Order a replacement queen if the queen is missing.

• Save Time and Money: Watch for Diseased Combs!

When putting your package into an empty hive or into a winter-killed colony, make sure **American foulbrood** was not present. It would, of course, be stupid to install your new package bees on combs infected with this disease.

A hive is infected with American foulbrood if it contains dead or decayed brood, or the dried-down, scaly remains of larvae or **pupae** lying *lengthwise* on the lower side of the cells. The scale adheres tightly to the wall of the cell (see Chapter 11, Diseases & Pests).

If in doubt, contact your local bee inspector to examine your hive.

• An Established Hive

If you received a hive full of bees, you will not have to do any of these preparations. The first thing you will need to do is move your hive to its permanent location.

A screened top should be nailed in place before moving bees in hot weather. You can nail it during the day, but cover it with an outer cover. When ready to move the bees at night, take off outer cover.

Moving Hives

Moving bees may be necessary to improve bee **forage,** avoid pesticide spraying, pollinate orchards, or diminish neighborhood complaints. Whatever the reasons, the hive parts must be secured together so they will not break apart during the move. Wooden parts may be fastened with **hive staples** or tied with plastic/nylon straps or bands. Remember, hives moved in the spring are lighter than fall hives, which are full of honey. To lighten the load, supers of honey can be removed.

Once secured, and the new location has been previously prepared, pick a calm evening that is not too hot. Bees can suffocate quickly in hot weather unless upper screened ventilation is supplied. By using a strip of screening, close off the entrance and tape any cracks or holes in the hive body; use smoke liberally. Lift onto vehicle and if possible, place hives so that **frames** are parallel with the road to prevent them sliding together.

Once installed at the new site, replace screen at the entrance with a handful of grass; this allows bees to gradually adjust to their new location. To avoid confusion by bees, they must be moved at least three miles (5km) from their original site. In a few days, inspect colony to make sure all is well.

See Chapter 3 for instructions about inspecting your hive.

6

2. Before You Start

Kinds of Bees

This chapter is for those who are buying bees for the first time.

Before you buy bees, determine the attributes of the different **races of bees** and their hybrids. This is similar to selecting a type of tomato or broccoli variety from seed catalogs.

There are three basic honey bee races in this country: **Italian, Caucasian** and **Carniolan.**

The Italian bees, *Apis mellifera ligustica,* are the most commonly used in the U.S.A. In general, they are a light colored race, with yellow and tan stripes. Fairly gentle, they are productive and not as prone to swarming as other races. They do, however, tend to rob weaker hives. Another problem is their susceptibility to **brood diseases** and their lower **winter hardiness;** but in general, they are good bees and will produce honey.

The Caucasians, *Apis mellifera caucasica* are a gentle race, with longer tongues and gray body hairs. While the darker queens are harder to spot, they are used in urban areas for their calm nature. About the only bad habit they have is their tendency to glue up or **propolize** the internal hive parts.

The last race, the Carniolan bees *Apis mellifera carnica,* are also dark with gray hairs. They are an extremely gentle race, quiet on the **comb** and winter hardy. Their one drawback is their tendency to swarm excessively.

All of these races can be cross bred and interbred to select for desirable traits and colors. Some of the well known and commercially available strains are **"Starline"** and **"Midnight"** Hybrids. The former is an Italian hybrid, whose queens are selected for greater egg laying capacity (more bees, more honey). The "Midnights", a combination of the two black bees (Caucasian and Carniolan), are also bred for production and gentleness.

Another hybrid, **"Buckfast"**, originally from England, was selected for gentleness and winter hardiness. Many commercial breeders have their own hybrid bees as well, bred for gentler nature, winter hardiness, and **disease resistance**. Some points to remember if you are thinking about purchasing them: they are more expensive than non-hybrid queens, and if the bees replace the queen themselves, called **supersedure**, the resulting new queen may not have those desirable characteristics you want.

Early Preparations

Before beginning in beekeeping, there are several things you must first do. Read everything you can find about bees in books, childrens' books, texts, and magazines. Then go and talk to beekeepers and attend bee meetings.

Almost any experienced beekeeper is ready to give an enthusiastic beginner a practical demonstration in manipulating a hive. The novice should work closely with several bee-keepers to develop handling tech-niques, and to pick up tips on equip-ment assembly. Remember, all bee-keepers will have their own way of doing things, and of course each one will be the *right way*.

It is advisable to start beekeeping in a small way at first. This will mini-mize the expense and disappointment should your bees have a bad season. Start with between two and five colo-nies. In this way, if you lose one queen, you can still save the bees by joining together the queenless hive with a **queenright** one.

Be wary of a beekeeper offering colonies for a ridiculously low price. They could be diseased or have some other problem not easily recognized by a beginner. If in doubt, call your local bee inspector or state agricul-ture department.

Equipment

Parts of A Bee Hive

The modern bee hive has elimi-nated the crude primitive methods of honey extraction and bee manipula-tion. Before moveable frames, bees were kept in straw baskets called **skeps**, or in hollowed logs, called **gums**. To collect the honey, beekeep-ers fumigated the bees with sulfur, which killed them, and cut out the wax combs that contained not only honey but **brood** and larvae. The re-sulting mess was not very appealing or sanitary by our standards, but did produce the only source of sweetening available.

Our modern hives were devel-oped from a simple discovery made famous by **Rev. L. L. Langstroth**. Building on the work of others, he found that bees would not build comb in a space less than 3/8" (9.5 mm). On the other hand, they will build excess comb, or **burr comb**, in spaces larger than that.

With the discovery of the **bee space**, Rev. Langstroth was able to construct a wooden frame to hold the honey combs, spaced in such a way that the bees would not fix them to-gether. This is called a **moveable frame**, and enables us to remove combs so we can examine the queen, the brood or the honey. In this way we no longer have to kill the bees to get their honey.

The parts of a modern hive con-sist of a box, or hive body, frames, bottom boards and covers. Refer to the illustration.

The *hive body* is a box without a cover and holds the frames. It comes in various heights, with matching

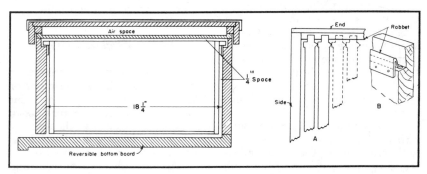

*The hive is so constructed that there is a **bee space** 3/8 - 1/4" (9.5mm) between the frames and around the inside of the hive. The bees will not build comb in spaces smaller than a bee space. USDA.*

Parts of a Modern Hive

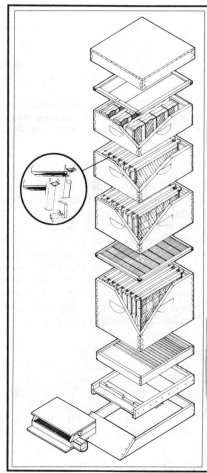

Telescoping Cover — Metal clad, fits over hive and protects supers below.

Ventilated Inner Cover — Includes ventilation port in rim for maximum air movement. Provides insulation and serves as an escape board.

Comb Honey Super — 4-5/8" deep. Various sizes and models available.

Shallow Super 5-11/16" deep — Used for surplus honey production or chunk honey. Several may be used per colony.

Frames — Sized to fit all supers.

Medium Depth Super 6-5/8" deep — Used for surplus honey production, chunk honey or even as a brood chamber.

Excluders — Placed between brood chamber and honey supers to contain queen.

Hive Body, Deep Super 9-1/2" deep — Used primarily as a brood box but can also be used as a honey super.

Slatted Rack — An optional board, placed above a standard bottom board. Reduces entrance congestion, improves ventilation.

Pollen Trap — A device to trap pollen in the summer.

Entrance Reducer or Cleat — Used to control the size of the opening at various times of the year.

Bottom Board — The base of the hive. It should not be placed on damp ground.

Hive Stand — Raises bottom board off the ground and provides bees with a landing area.

frames. The four common hive depths used in this country are the *full* or *standard* depth, the *three-quarter*, the *half* and the *shallow* depths.

The Standard depth, which is 9-1/2" deep is used mostly as two units, for the brood nest. Such a double story gives the queen space to lay many eggs which makes the resulting colony very strong.

To collect honey, beekeepers use a smaller hive body. These are then called **honey supers** and come in three sizes. The medium or three quarters depth, is 6-5/8" and is used

mostly for **extracted** honey (that means the frames are spun out in a centrifuge or **extractor**). Some beekeepers use only one size of super for both brood and honey; in this way they do not have to change equipment. These first two sizes already mentioned, are the most common for this kind of use.

The next two sizes of supers are the half depth, at 5-11/16" and the section or shallow super, 4-5/8". These supers are used for honey that can either be extracted or used in **comb honey** production.

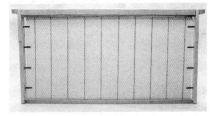

Two sizes of frames. Left, the deep frame has vertical wires for added strength. The smaller frame, above, is used for cut comb honey.

The Hoffman self-spacing frames have projections on the end bars. One edge is V-shaped and the other squared, to help keep propolizing to a minimum. This super is equipped with a stoller spacer to evenly space frames across the hive.

The *frames* are made to correspond with the super depths. A commonly made frame is called the **Hoffmann self-spacing frame** and is separated from each other with a notch to keep the bee space exact. Suspended in the hive are 9 or 10 frames. A bee space separates the frames from the walls, tops and bottoms of the supers. This will prevent the bees from gluing down, or propolizing, the frames.

The hive sits on a board, called a **bottom board**, complete with a cleat or **entrance reducer.** During hot weather, the cleat is taken out entirely for better air circulation. In cold weather, the cleat is inserted to restrict the opening.

The bottom board sits on some kind of **hive stand**, to keep it off the damp ground, and to minimize the problems of some pests.

There are usually two covers on a bee hive: the inner cover, which is placed over the top super, and the outer cover. If used, the inner cover provides insulation and serves as an **escape board.** The outer cover telescopes over the sides and front of the hive, to protect it from rain. Some western states and larger commercial bee operations use only one cover, called the **migratory** cover.

•Frame Construction

Wooden frames should be carefully constructed so they will not break apart. A well-made frame should last you 10 or more years.

Nail together each frame using all 8 nails. Sometimes during hive in-

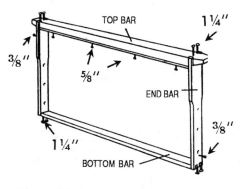

Nail in all eight nails as shown. For added strength, glue or staples may be also used. To keep top bars from pulling off, nail in two more nails through the end bars into the top bar.

spections, the top bar of the frame is pulled off when you pry it out of the hive. To prevent this, nail in two extra nails perpendicular to the top bar, through the end bars.

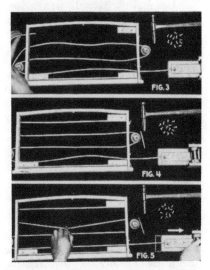

Thread wire through holes in end bars, being careful not to crimp the wire. Wrap one end of wire around a small nail, then drive it flush. Tighten all wires carefully, until taut, then wrap other end of wire around a small nail and drive home.

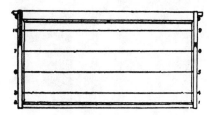

A frame wired with 4 horizontal wires is used for extracted honey or brood rearing. Use heavy, wired foundation in such frames.

If you wish to wire the frames, first put it together and insert the **metal eyelets** in the holes of the end bars. This will keep the wire from biting into the wood.

Remember, GOOD FRAMES MAKE GOOD COMBS. Crooked, sagging combs and those full of drone cells are wasteful in a productive colony, and could lead to swarming. They can be prevented by careful construction of the frames, as well as firm placement of the wax foundation.

•Foundation

In addition to the hives and frames, you will need **foundation**. This is a thin sheet of pure beeswax, embossed in such a way that it will have the imprint of the hexagonal honeycomb. If you picture a comb with the cell walls scraped down to the midrib, you have a good idea what foundation looks like.

Comb foundation serves a four-

Once the frame is put together, you can add the foundation sheet. Pull off the wedge at the top bar. Slide sheet into the bottom bar groove, then slip top into top bar groove. Make sure the wire hooks are at the top, and fit in the wedge with the hooks pointing outward. Hammer wedge in place.

11

fold purpose: 1) It furnishes a considerable part of the beeswax required by the bees (this relieves the bees from making all the comb, and saves you honey). 2) It centers the comb in the frames. 3) It comes in 2 sizes, one for rearing **worker** bees and one for **drones**. This means you can somewhat control their worker and drone population. 4) It enables bees to draw out a frame more rapidly (greater surface area), than they would be able to do otherwise.

Frames destined for the **brood-nest** or the honey extractor should have foundation reinforced with wires. If not, the comb may sag, be crooked or bent (resulting in deformed comb and wasted space) or it could simply break apart during extraction.

Reinforced Foundation

When purchasing foundation, buy extra thick, **wired foundation** for brood and honey combs. Vertical wires are already embedded in the wax and provide good support. To give more strength to these frames, however, it is good practice to wire the frames with horizontal wires before installing the foundation.

Frame wire is strung between the two end bars through the holes reinforced with metal eyelets. Draw the

wire very tight, and secure each end around small nails. When finished, drive in the nails flush with the wood. There are several wiring devices sold, so check bee supply catalogs.

Use four horizontal wires in deep frames for all types of foundation and two in shallower frames.

Successful Drawn Foundation

Foundation will NOT be drawn out by bees unless there is a good source of nectar coming in. Nectar (food) should be supplied to newly installed packages or swarms in the form of sugar syrup (see Chapter 1, Installing a Package). If the colony is populous and has ample food, supplemental feeding may not be needed. Group foundation frames together, or into one super, rather than placing them here and there in the hive. Remove any half-drawn frames before winter, or the bees may chew them. Remember, for best results, *there should be a strong **nectar flow**.*

•The Bee Smoker

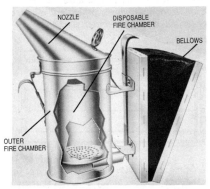

Smokers that come with a disposable inner chamber will last longer. Pump the bellows to ignite the fuel, then close the top so smoke can be directed through the nozzle.

A **smoker** is considered to be the most important piece of beekeeping equipment. Without it one would have great difficulty in handling the

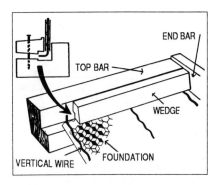

A close-up view of the wire hooks fitting into the top bar wedge groove.

bees. It consists of a *fire box* or little stove, mounted on a bellows. Slow burning fuel, preferably dry rotten wood, chips, burlap and corn cobs make good quality smoke. Smoke stimulates the bees to gorge honey. While they are doing that, they're not flying about or stinging you. It also masks any alarm scent the bees may give off. *Too much smoke*, however, will make the bees panic, run on the combs, and fly off. The proper amount of smoke to use comes with experience.

•Protection

Stings need not be a threat to anyone because of the protective clothing that is available. The development and use of **desensitizing injections** are also available for those rare individuals who are truly allergic to honey bee venom.

Beginning beekeepers vary in their ability to work with honey bees. Some people take to beekeeping so naturally that the prospect of receiving an occasional sting is of no concern to them. Others begin their first encounters tense, and their movements lack the smoothness and efficiency of the confident. Confidence comes with experience and practice, and usually results in less disturbance to the colony (and fewer stings).

Every beekeeper should wear a **veil** at all times. Bees instinctively attack the face when agitated, and stings in this area are painful and dangerous.

The beginner will feel more confident if attired in a suit of white **coveralls** with a zipped-on veil. The white coverall represents a non-threatening intruder which the bees will respond to calmly, and it will also keep your clothes clean. Dressed in this manner, you are virtually sting-proof.

Gloves will give you more security, but with experience, can be put aside except in emergencies. You can

A one-piece bee suit with zip-on veil makes you virtually sting proof. Tighten cuffs at the ankles with a strap.

actually receive MORE stings with gloves on.

If you don't wear a coverall, avoid dark, woolen or fuzzy fabrics and wear light colored, loose-fitting clothing with a smooth texture.

•Hive Tool

Hive tools are indispensable for prying off covers and supers, removing frames and staples, and for scraping **propolis** and **burr comb**. There are various styles and sizes, but be-

Standard hive tools, also sold as scrapers, are used to pry apart hive bodies and frames, and clean off burr comb.

fore you buy, talk with other beekeepers, and try out some of their hive tools. It is also a good idea to buy SEVERAL hive tools, since you can easily misplace one in the grass. They should be sanded, sharpened and marked with red paint annually.

• Accessory Equipment

Queen Excluders

There are several styles of **queen excluders**. Most will do what the name suggests — prevent the queen from passing through and laying eggs where she is not wanted. While a queen excluder may serve several functions around the apiary, it's primary purpose is to confine the queen to the brood nest.

Queen excluder grids allow worker bees to pass through, but keep out drones and queens.

It is possible to do without a queen excluder, but some of the disadvantages should be taken into consideration. Without one, the queen will invariably lay eggs in a small section of a honey super. This becomes a nuisance when removing honey for extracting and it becomes impossible to avoid getting brood mixed in with the extracted honey, which is unsanitary. With brood in the extracting supers, it is nearly impossible to rid the combs of bees using bee escapes. Rearing brood in extracting frames also darkens the comb, which is a factor in the discoloring of light colored honeys.

Remember, queen excluders also exclude drones. To prevent a buildup of dead drones in the top supers, provide an upper exit hole for them. This can be made by drilling an auger hole into the upper hive body.

Bee Escapes and Escape Boards

The **bee escape** is a little device, consisting of two pairs of sensitive

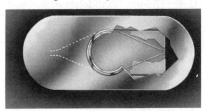

Bee Escapes have two V-shaped prongs made of thin metal strips. They can spread apart to let a single bee pass out but not back in. Place in oblong hole of inner cover or other escape board, with the hole up. Photo below shows bee escape in place.

springs, which allows bees to pass through only one way (see illus.). It is mounted in the oval hole of the inner cover. When a crop of honey is ready to be removed, the inner cover with the bee escape device in place, is put *underneath* the honey supers. The escape permits the bees above to exit to the warmer broodnest, but will not let them back up. When used in this way, the inner cover is called an escape board. There are other types of escape boards on the market, some with larger or greater numbers of bee escape devices.

For more discussion on using escape boards, refer to Chapter 7; Harvesting.

How To Get Bees

There are several ways a beginning beekeeper can obtain bees. These include: buying a nucleus hive, a full hive, capturing swarms or buying a package. Bees can also be removed from buildings or trees, but this is not recommended for beginners.

Purchasing Bee Hives and Nucs

Some beekeepers will sell you **hives** already full of bees. In this way you have a hive ready to go, one that will build up quickly and will give you a good crop of honey.

Be sure the bees are disease and pest free — certified by the **state inspector**. Bee **diseases** are carried in old wax combs and honey, and may not be evident to a beginner. Also, old, mismatched equipment could cost you time and labor. Check to make sure all the equipment is in reasonable shape, and will last you many years. You will have to move your hive to your own **apiary**, which could be quite a problem if the colony is full of honey. (See Chap 1, Moving Bees).

When purchasing a hive of bees, make sure you have at least one deep super full of bees and one of drawn comb with some honey. Check for diseases, pests and condition of equipment.

Call your local apiary inspector concerning the movement of bees on combs in or out of your state or county. Some beekeepers prefer to start by buying a **nucleus hive**, or **nuc** (see photo on following page). This consists of a small box (only 3-5 frames) of bees, a laying queen, and brood. It is easy to transport and install. Again, ask for proof of compliance with local bee inspections, disease and pest ordinances and shipping regulations. You merely place the frames into a larger hive, with frames of foundation or **drawn comb**, and feed.

Buying Packages

Buying bees by the pound in a package is the most convenient way for the beginner to start. Two to six pound packages with or without queens are available. To begin a colony, order the package (with queen) early in the year - January or February. Under favorable conditions, a two

Nucs or nucleus hives are 3-5 frames of bees, brood and a laying queen. They are easily made from scrap lumber and are handy to have for swarms or queen rearing operations. Many beekeepers sell starter nucs.

pound package will grow to a strong colony. However, the larger the package, the better off and faster it will grow. Package bee shippers are listed in beekeeping journals. If you write for a sample of *Gleanings in Bee Culture*, P.O. Box 706, Medina, OH 44258, you can secure the addresses of package bee and queen shippers.

Package bees are shaken from colonies into **shipping cages** made of wire and wood, convenient for shipping and handling. Each package is comparable to a moderate-sized swarm.

Unless otherwise specified, a newly-mated queen bee is confined within a small cage which accompa-

nies each package. Each shipping cage is supplied with a can containing sugar syrup. This feeds the bees for several days while they journey to their new home.

Packages are shipped from the Southern states where there are wide regions well adapted to the production of package bees. Conditions needed to produce bees and queens require a light and continuous **honey flow** throughout the bee season, a mild winter and an early spring.

Producers of package bees manage their colonies for large population build-up as early as mid-March. Preparation for filling packages includes shaking frames of bees into a funnel.

After weighing the bees, they will be funneled into waiting packages. They come with and without queens and are shipped through the post office.

Bees are shaken into packages from strong colonies. This is usually done in the afternoon when the older foraging bees and many of the drones are away from the hive. This means the packages are composed of mostly young worker bees, as drones and older workers do not aid in rapid colony growth.

When ordering packages, make sure they advertise disease and mite-free bees. There are several pests and diseases that are carried by bees; for a further discussion see Chapter 11; Diseases & Pests.

•When to Get Packages

There is no advantage in getting packages too early in the spring. Cool weather and lack of adequate flowers will kill small packages or set them back too far to make a strong colony. It takes seven or eight weeks for packages to build up to full strength colonies, ready for the main honey flow. Have your packages arrive in time for the dandelion/fruit bloom.

The critical time in the development of a package is during the first three weeks. It takes three weeks from the time the queen begins to lay until new young bees emerge. Two weeks more, these young bees will be foragers; this makes it five weeks before there are young bees of honey-gathering age. When young bees begin to emerge, package colonies will forge ahead, if the weather and the conditions for obtaining nectar and pollen are favorable.

Most Profitable Size of Package

In the Northwest, where the honey flow comes rather late and is long drawn out, two-pound packages give good results. In the white clover and alsike regions, where there is no sweet clover or alfalfa, three-pound packages are preferred, because it is necessary to have colonies up to the peak at the time the main honey flow starts. Frequently, a honey flow from alsike clover does not last over two or three weeks. It is very important to continuously feed your package sugar syrup for the first three weeks. If in doubt, order a larger package, 3-5 pounds.

Importance of Good Queens

It is extremely important to have a good queen with each package. The cage containing the queen and a few attendant bees is suspended within the cluster of the package. A queen that has been properly reared from good stock, was properly handled and shipped will likely do well.

Some queens begin to fail shortly after package installation, and the bees proceed to rear another. In such cases, another laying queen should be introduced as soon as possible (see Chapter 9, Requeening).

Queenless Packages

It is possible to order a package without a queen. Some beekeepers like to give their newly established packages a "booster package" about two to three weeks after installation. Others order queenless five pound packages to use in pollination or for queen rearing activities. Talk to experienced beekeepers to find out how else to use a queenless package.

To obtain bees from swarms, bee trees or from buildings, see Chapter 8.

Locating Your Apiary

Honey bees are very versatile in using the resources of many kinds of environments, from the tropics to within a few hundred miles of the Arctic Circle. Of course, some areas are more favorable than others. A moderate climate and ample flowers from which to gather nectar and **pollen,** increases the likelihood of a colony producing a **surplus of honey**.

Honey bees may be placed on city lots, suburban acreage or on farms. The most important precaution to remember is to not place your bees where their **flight path** will cross a neighbor's garden, pool, walk or other space where their presence may cause a nuisance. As a precaution, we sug-

gest you check your local ordinances for any restrictions on keeping bees. We also recommend you check registration requirements for bees in your state. (That and other information pertaining to beekeeping in your state may be obtained by requesting a copy of "Who's Who in Beekeeping", printed annually in *Gleanings in Bee Culture,* a monthly beekeeping magazine published by The A.I. Root Company.)

Facts To Consider

Bees seem to do best in a location that gets morning sun, afternoon shade and north-wind protection. If you live in a hot climate, bees should be given light daytime shade. Sheds or sheltering trees provide needed shade in hot arid regions. A nearby water source is also mandatory, so the bees can cool the interior of their hives (see below, Water for Bees).

On the other hand, in cooler climates, bees will get out earlier if their entrances face S.E., to catch the early morning sun. By noon, however, they should have some shade protection. In wintertime, the colonies should have all day sun and northern wind breaks. These can be snow fences, buildings, or a living hedge such as shrubs and evergreens.

•Water for Bees

Bees keep their hive cool in summer by fanning and evaporating droplets of water. This air conditioning is needed to keep the wax combs from melting and to provide constant humidity. The closer the water source, the happier the bees, and the less time they spend looking for it. Nectar supplies some of this needed moisture, but on hot, dry summer days, additional water will be needed.

Train your bees in the spring to a water source by filling it with a light syrup. Once trained, they will *always* expect to find water there. You can

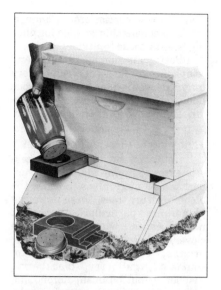

Boardman Feeders can be filled with water during the summer to keep bees out of neighboring pools and bird baths.

supply water by means of a dripping faucet, a tank or bucket of water (covered with floating wood or cork chips), or by feeding water. **Boardman type** (front entrance) or internal **feeders** can be filled with water. Replenish with clean water when empty. If your source of water is allowed to dry, the bees will find another source. This can be troublesome if it happens to be your neighbors' bird bath or swimming pool. NEVER let your water source become dry.

Bees In Town

Bees can be kept successfully in residential communities, even on small lots in densely populated neighborhoods. Check local ordinances that may restrict the keeping of bees.

There is one drawback to the backyard location, however — the bees may cause some annoyance if the neighborhood is thickly settled. At times, bees will sting, and most people fear them and would rather not have them around. Build a fence barrier or plant high shrubs to deflect the flight line of the field bees over or away from paths or centers of activity of near neighbors. Allow as much space as possible between the hives and residences, patios, pools and walks. Provide a fresh water source for your bees to keep them from drinking out of neighboring pools or bird baths.

Keep nearby residents informed about the benefits of having bees in the neighborhood, stress the pollination role of the honey bee. Remind them your bees are filling a niche that *could* be occupied by the more notorious **hornets, wasps,** or **yellow jackets.**

Avoid handling bees when doing so will antagonize them — early or late in the day or on days when there is no honey flow. Assure your neighbors, if they seem the least bit doubtful, that the sting is principally a defensive measure, seldom used unless bees are provoked.

Obtain queens that are known for gentleness, and requeen those hives which seem continuously irritable. A young, gentle queen can change the temperament of an irascible colony almost immediately. For a more complete discussion on this topic, see Chapter 12, Beekeeping in Residential Neighborhoods.

Gifts of honey distributed through the neighborhood will do wonders to "sweeten" any apprehensive feelings about having bees in the neighborhood.

If your residential area is not suitable, or beekeeping is not permitted, seek locations elsewhere. A small ad placed in the classified section of your newspaper may bring several invitations to have your bees placed on nearby farms. Many urban areas are adjacent to farms which grow specialized vegetables or small fruits; these could be good locations.

Choosing An Apiary Site

An **apiary,** or area where beehives are located, should be carefully selected. Assess the location, taking into consideration the vulnerability of bees to toxic sprays. Do not locate near crops known to need spraying, such as sweet corn or fruit orchards. Select a location that can be reached by a wheeled vehicle, even during inclement weather. Avoid isolated locations from which hives can be vandalized or stolen. Avoid swampy ground or low lying land that may be flooded by nearby streams.

Always respect the property on which you have your bees, even though it may be that of a friend or relative. Small payments of honey are usually welcomed, and are well worth the small cost for the goodwill of the landowner. **Pollination** benefits sometimes make this small compensation unnecessary, particularly when a grower needs bees for production of a commercial crop. Commercial beekeepers charge a fee for placing bees in these locations.

Post your name, address, and telephone number in each apiary **outyard** (bees located away from your house). Notify your state bee inspector of the *exact* location of each yard.

•Locating For Honey Production

An apiary surrounded with several acres of **honey plants** may support ten or more hives. Besides the bloom of fruit trees, these flowering plants are particularly important nectar-bearers: white clover, alsike clover, sweet clover, alfalfa, sage, orange, tupelo, saw palmetto, sourwood, gallberry, blackberry, raspberry, button-bush, horehound, sumac, mustard, basswood, maple, willow, tulip poplar, goldenrod, milkweed, fireweed, boneset, aster, mesquite, and catsclaw (see Chapter 6, Honey Plants and Pollination).

3. Your First Inspection

Examining Your Package

After seven to ten days, you should examine your new colony to see if everything is fine.

It is important to select a warm day for this, between the hours of ten and three o'clock. Don't open a hive on a cool or chilly day, late in the afternoon or after a cool rain. A strong colony is apt to be more irritable than a small one under adverse conditions.

Once a piece of newspaper is lit, pump bellows and add smoker fuel. Keep pumping to light fuel, then close top. Kennerly Photo.

First of all, light your smoker so that it will stay lighted. Here is how:

Lighting— Begin by crumbling paper into a ball about the size of your fist. Light it and drop into the canister. Add solid fuel gradually as the paper burns and ignites the fuel. Pump the bellows slowly as the fuel ignites. When burning well, finish filling the canister with fuel, and close the lid. This will extinguish any flame and cause the fuel to continue to smolder.

Too much fuel at the beginning will put out the fire. Working the **bellows** will force a draft of air through the burning fuel and make good smoke.

Give several puffs with the bellows to be sure that the fire is started, but do not start a blaze. Make sure there is enough smoldering fire in the fuel so it will not go out while you are handling the bees.

Fuel — Many types of fuel are satisfactory to use in your smoker but some are better than others. Dry wood, wood chips, pine needles or cones, burlap bags (which have not been treated with insecticides), corn cobs, and cotton cloth will all give good smoke. Avoid chemical fluids, charcoal or other fuels giving high heat during combustion.

Protection — You may want to protect your hands with long-sleeved gloves. Put on your bee veil and make it bee tight. Wear loose, light-colored clothing, avoiding black or fuzzy material of any kind. Trousers should be tucked in the socks, tied or taped about your ankles.

To Avoid Stings

1. Dress according to your experience and competence in handling bees, the bees' temper, and according to your sensitivity to stings. *Always wear a veil.*
2. Light the smoker and keep it working strongly. Don't oversmoke but don't hesitate to use the smoker vigorously to keep the bees under control. Experience will teach you just how much

Properly dressed beekeepers wearing veils, light clothing and perhaps gloves. Stand to the side and back of the hive, and hold frame over the top bars.

smoke to use.

3. Keep movements slow and deliberate. As you gain experience your skill and speed working with bees will improve.

4. Whenever possible, work your bees during warm, sunny days near the middle of the day. Avoid cool periods when a nectar flow has been interrupted, or showery, hot and humid days when the bees are not flying. Don't work bees early in the morning, evenings or nights.

5. Bees are sensitive to strong odors and vibrations. So don't wear strong smelling perfumes, aftershaves or hair spray, and don't bump or knock on the hive. They also resent obstructions in their flight paths, especially the few feet directly in front of the entrance; NEVER stand directly in front of a hive when working it.

6. Avoid pinching or crushing bees. This releases an **alarm odor** which alerts bees to sting.

After you are Stung

If you are stung, immediately brush or scrape off the **sting sac.** The bee's sting has a **poison sac** at its base from which poison is pumped and moved deeper into the wound, even after the sting is detached from the bee. By swiftly brushing or scraping off the sting (rather than picking it off) no pressure is put on the poison sac, and thus no poison is forced into the wound.

There is no known cure for stings. Medicinal applications are usually ineffective because the puncture wound is too small. An anti-itch spray or cream can be applied later. The secret is to minimize the *amount* of poison with each bee sting. In cases of severe swelling or reaction to a sting, see your physician.

Opening the Hive

Whenever smoke is needed, pump the bellows slowly. (Working the bellows faster increases combustion and creates hot ash.) Use only enough smoke to control the bees.

Bees respond to smoke by filling their **honey sacs** with honey. In addition, it is believed that smoke interferes with the communication of alarm odors. Smoke does not sedate the bees or cause them undue distress, providing it is used with discre-

Bees sting to protect their colony. Scrape away sting with a hive tool or fingernail. Doering Photo.

Before opening your hive, blow smoke at the entrance to subdue guard bees.

tion and only when needed.

With hive tool in (gloved) hand, and veil on tight, approach your colony from the side or rear. Avoid standing in front of the entrance or getting in the line of flight of the bees.

Blow three or four puffs of smoke into the entrance of the hive to subdue the **guard bees;** don't overdo this. If you over-smoke, the bees may stampede, making them more difficult to control.

Take off the **outer cover** as gently as possible: the less the bees are jarred or aroused, the easier your task will be.

Blow smoke into inner cover hole, then use your hive tool to pry it up.

Take the hive tool and gently pry up the inner cover. It may be necessary to pry up more than one corner to unstick it. Through the gap between the inner cover and hive, blow in a

After blowing smoke under the inner cover, gently lift it off, and place it in front of the entrance.

couple of puffs of smoke. Let the inner cover down for a moment then gently lift it up again. Puff two or three light puffs on top of the open super, just

enough smoke to drive the bees on top down between the frames. Whenever many of the bees' heads are seen sticking up between the frames, give them a little more smoke.

Bees will usually give ample warning when they are about to fly up and sting: when they come up between the frames immediately after being driven down with smoke; when they act nervous, twitching their bodies nervously; or when they line up head to head between the tops of the frames. At the sign of any of these behaviors give them a good puff of smoke to keep them down. If helpers are available, have them work the smoker while you do the work. If your bees seem very cross, close up the hive and wait until another day when bees are better natured.

Take care while you are working not to pinch or kill any bees. This releases an alarm odor called **alarm pheromone.** If you smell something like banana oil, this is the alarm pheromone. Close up your hive and wait for a better day.

Carefully place your fingers only where there are no bees. If bees are very numerous, simply push them over to one side with your (gloved) fingers, being careful not to pinch them in the process. Always remember, make *slow-motion* movements. Be *deliberate* and *cool* in the manipulation of bees.

After you have opened the hives a few times, you will be able to discard the gloves; they are somewhat clumsy and may even lead to more stings.

Handling Frames

Once the inner cover is removed, crowd the frames together so you have room to lift out the one nearest you. By using your hive tool to scrape away **wax** or **propolis,** you should be able to pry out the first frame.

It is better to take out completely

After taking out an end frame, loosen other frames so you can remove them gently, without pinching the bees.

To examine the frame, hold it by top bar and examine one side. Slowly flip it up to examine the other side.

the first frame to give you more room. The end frames are usually too cool for brood and unless the queen is cramped for space, it will be full of honey or pollen. To make the job easier, the first frame or two removed from the hive may be set down on the ground and leaned against the hive at the back or near, but not blocking, the entrance. Lift the frame straight up by taking hold of both ends of the top bar. Don't scrape it against other frames as you remove it; you could kill many bees this way. Hold the frame over the hive (so bees falling off will land inside the hive and not on your feet) and examine the frame. To look at the other side, slowly flip the frame up, so the top bar is now on the bottom.

Work With the Queen

Before you open your hive, ask yourself, "What am I looking for?"

Your answer should be among these: To see if the queen is laying well; to see that brood-rearing is progressing satisfactorily; to make sure the bees have sufficient food; to check for signs of a honey flow; to add more room; to take off supers filled with honey; or to prepare the colony for winter.

You should make sure that each hive has a laying queen. Examine the hive whenever you have reason to suspect that anything may have gone wrong with the queen (see Chapter 9, Sudden Queen Loss).

How to Find the Queen

A queen is much easier to find some periods of the year than others. During the spring and summer, in the height of her egg laying, her **abdomen** is swollen with eggs and she appears very large. Some queens, especially Italians, have long, yellow abdomens while their worker bees have tan and yellow bands. Such a queen is very

Notice the longer abdomen of this laying queen, and her lack of stripes. She and her daughter workers are resting on top of capped worker brood.

conspicuous on the comb. A dark queen with little or no yellow will be harder to find. This is why some breeders dab a little paint on the queen's thorax.

Usually a queen can be located by the behavior of the bees around her. When she is standing still, there will be a conspicuous ring of workers all around her, some licking her, some offering her food.

When she moves over the combs, this "ring of attendants" will not be visible, and she may be more difficult to spot. Even if you do not find the queen, all you need to find are **eggs** and young larvae. If you find no eggs, no young larvae, and there are **queen cells** started, you can be reasonably

Notice how this "ring" of attendant worker bees surrounding the queen gives away her presence. This only happens when the queen is at rest.

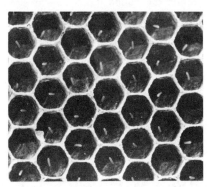

At the bottom of each cell, you should see a single egg. This is a good sign that you have a laying queen and you need not look further for her. E. F. Bigelow Photo.

sure that there is no queen in the hive. It is a waste of time to hunt for her under these conditions, especially if queen cells are fairly well advanced.

If, on the other hand, you find eggs and larvae in all stages of growth, you can assume that the queen is present. Usually, she will be found on the combs containing mostly eggs and young larvae. When you intend to look for the queen, use only very little smoke; too much will cause the bees to run. For that reason work them on a warm day, when the bees are quiet and need little or no smoke.

Also, look for the queen in the middle of the day, when most of the field bees are outside. If you attempt to find her toward night, when all the bees are in the hive, the task will be much more difficult.

Some strains of bees are very nervous and run over the combs as they are being inspected. A running queen is difficult to find. Requeen such a colony with a calmer one.

If, at any time, the queen cannot be found, even under favorable conditions, the best thing to do is to close up the hive and try again the next day.

If the Queen is Lost

If by any accident the queen should be lost, the bees soon detect her absence and set up a peculiar buzzing of distress. Then they begin to make a new queen by constructing queen cells. If there are lots of 3-day old larvae, queen cells will be built anywhere on the comb.

Colonies can become queenless without your knowledge. Unless you chance to notice them at the time of the loss, their behavior would hardly be striking enough to attract your attention. Still, if you see bees standing idly about the entrance, and the foragers are not bringing in pollen when the bees from other colonies are doing so, you should examine that colony. If plenty of eggs and **worker**

brood are found, then the queen is present, and it is not necessary to look further. If queen cells, and no eggs but **capped** worker brood are found, they may be preparing to swarm. If a *few* **queen cells** and a little scattering of worker and drone brood are found, the bees are probably trying to supersede (or replace) a queen they consider defective. If only **drone brood** is present, or you find many eggs scattered in each cell, the colony has either a **drone-laying queen** or **laying workers.** This colony should be joined with another or a new queen introduced, as it is doomed (see Chapter 9; Requeening).

Supersedure

An occasional problem with package bees is the failure of the queen. This may be due to injury or disease. The bees usually raise another to take her place while she is still alive. In this instance, the queen mother and her daughter will live side by side for a time.

Queen cells appearing on the face of the comb, among worker cells, are called supersedure cells. This means the bees are trying to replace a diseased, old, or injured queen. Penn. State Univ. Photo.

In supersedure, you have two choices. You may either leave these cells which will produce a new queen, or you can **requeen** the colony yourself. Sometimes only one or two queen-cells are built for supersedure (see Chapter 1, Package Failures).

If the colony is very weak, unite it with a stronger one, rather than wasting its resources raising a new queen. Destroy all queen cells before you join it. Later, if the new colony becomes very strong, you can **split** it and regain your lost hive.

Importance of Good Queens
The queen is the single most important factor in the build-up of each colony. A young vigorous queen, capable of laying a compact pattern of brood in at least six to eight combs, will raise the population rapidly while nectar and pollen are available. Some systems of beekeeping call for queen replacement every year; others count on productive queens to last for two seasons. For others, queen replace-ment is handled on an individual colony basis; when a colony is not productive it should receive a new queen.

Colonies Short of Food
One of the most critical factors to keep track of is the presence of food in the colony. While you are examining the frames, be alert for signs of starvation. You should see yellow **pollen pellets** packed in the comb. They supply bees with needed **protein**. Liquid drops of both nectar and capped honey should also be visible in the comb.

Each frame in the brood nest should contain eggs, brood, honey and pollen. In the center of the frame, look for eggs/larvae and brood. Surrounding this is a line of pollen, then honey.

If you do not see any pollen or nectar drops, *you must feed* the colony now. Close the hive and immediately make up some syrup (2:1 sugar:water), and feed, feed, feed. You will be amazed at the difference in

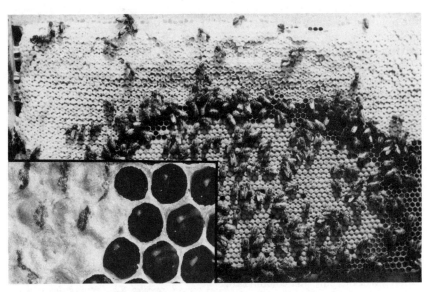

A frame of capped brood (center) surrounded by capped honey. D. Bone Photo. The close-up shows capped and uncapped honey.

temper, morale and attitude of the bees once they are given food.

Bees cannot raise brood with honey alone. If there is very little stored pollen in the combs, a **pollen substitute** may be needed. Bees starved of protein will eat eggs and will pull out larvae and pupae from their cells. They will dump them outside the entrance of the hive. If you see dead immature bees like this, do not even open the hive. Go immediately and mix the bees syrup and pollen substitute.

The ingredients for a pollen substitute can be obtained from bee supply houses. There are many kinds of substitutes containing a yeast, soy or dairy by-product, but not pollen. Mix to a dough-like consistency with sugar syrup, and shape into a cake about the size of your hand. Place it on a piece of wax paper and turn it, cake down, on the top bars just above the brood nest. Check back in a week. If they have eaten most of the cake, give them more. Stop feeding when the bees are bringing in natural pollen.

You may also feed natural pollen that you trapped yourself. Do not feed commercially produced honey or pollen, as they could contain disease spores.

Normal Build-Up

As a rule, normal colonies that have had all the necessary requirements build up rapidly. In many regions of the country where there is a fruit and dandelion honey flow, it is amazing how rapidly colonies build up. When all of the frames in the first body are full of bees, honey and brood, it is time to give them another super. With a package, it is best to give them another deep super to raise more brood, so the colony can be very strong for the main summer honey flow. Most people give two deep supers for brood, and use shallows for honey.

Swarming

Where do new bee colonies come from? They don't last forever and must duplicate themselves in order to survive. They do this by swarming. This means that the colony will grow so large that it will split in half. The old queen will fly out with the swarm and begin a new colony in another location.

Meanwhile, the original colony, now queenless, has made some new queens. They do this by feeding selected worker larvae with the high protein substance, royal jelly. With this special food, the young larvae soon grow so huge that a large, peanut-like cell is constructed. This queen cell contains a virgin queen which will hatch in sixteen days (workers hatch in twenty-one, drones in twenty-four). When she is about a week old, the virgin queen will fly outside the hive in search of drones (male bees). They mate in the air; one queen will mate with ten or more drones, who die shortly afterwards. Once mated, the queen will not leave the hive again, unless she too swarms.

Closing Up

Once you have made all these observations — queen, brood and food stores, you should now close up the bees and leave them alone, except to feed, for another 2-3 weeks.

When ready to close, space the frames evenly across the super and put on the inner cover. Fill the feeder jars, put on the protecting empty super and the outer cover, then a rock or other weight. This inspection should last only 15-20 minutes per colony. Any longer than that, and you are wasting time and disrupting the bees.

Beginners especially tend to dis-

When you close up your hive, make sure the supers fit exactly together, and a weight is placed on top to keep cover from blowing off.

turb a package too often. This has adverse affects on colony morale and could weaken the hive. Be content with quietly sitting next to the hive and observing the incoming foragers, or set up an observation hive. As long as they are busy bringing in nectar (which you can't see) and pollen, all is well.

Inspecting an Established Hive

Once you have moved your hive to the apiary, wait a few days for them to settle down, then open. If the equipment is in good shape, (no holes in the hive bodies, broken frames or covers), all you need to do is see if the queen has enough space to lay her eggs.

(A) In the spring most bees and brood are in the top supers. To provide room for the queen, place supers full of bees/brood on bottom. (B) Then, stack empty supers above bees. Drawing by D. Sammataro.

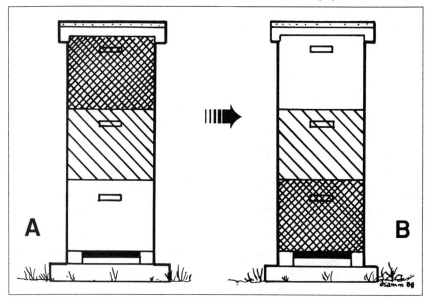

Get your smoker going, and smoke as you would normally (see section on Opening the Hive). Take off covers and quickly look in the upper honey supers, if you have any. If they are full of bees, the queen may be laying in it. If you intend to use this for honey, you must get the queen out. You do this by **reversing** the supers (see illustration on previous page).

Reversing

If the queen and brood are in an upper super, place all the frames of brood into one super, and put it aside. Remove all remaining supers down to the bottom board. Put the super of brood, bees and queen on the bottom board. Above this, place your empty deep brood super. The queen will move up into the brood chambers to lay her eggs as long as there are empty frames for her. In the next two weeks, the brood below will emerge from the super below. Once empty, it can then be removed and put above for brood nest expansion or honey storage.

If the colony had only two deep supers, reverse as follows:

In the spring, most of the brood will be in the upper brood chamber of a two story colony. The upper box will have five or more frames of brood/bees. The lower box will be empty of brood and scattered with honey. To increase the amount of space for brood rearing, reverse the position of the upper and lower hive bodies. Repeat this procedure in ten days, or after the queen has filled the empty combs with eggs.

Once the two supers are full of brood and bees, use a queen excluder and place honey supers on top (see Chapter 5, Your First Honey Flow).

4. Getting to Know Your Bees

The Honey Bee Colony

The **Honey Bee,** (*Apis mellifera* L.) whose Latin name means Honey Maker, is one of the most beneficial insects in the world. Not only do they give us beeswax, which is used mostly in cosmetics today, but they have also provided the sweetness of honey for thousands of years. Most valuable of all, however, is the fact that they contribute to the pollination of the flowers they visit.

City of Bees

A colony of bees, which includes a *queen* mother, some *drones* or male bees, and many *workers*, has been compared to a city in the way it functions. Here's how.

Cities have an organized system of streets and buildings, refuse pickup, and policing. Bee colonies have the same. Their beeswax combs are the living quarters, food storage and passageways for the inhabitants. House bees regularly patrol the streets and passages for debris and litter. When they find any, it is usually discarded outside. If it is too big to move (like a dead mouse) it may be covered over with a impermeable layer of glue (called propolis). This stops it from decomposing and thus spoiling the nest. Guard bees are also on duty, checking each bee at the entrance to make sure it belongs to the colony, and alerting other bees if intruders are present.

Bee cities go further since they can control the temperature, humidity and air flow year round inside the hive. The reason for such control is the building material used: **beeswax**. If the internal hive temperature gets too hot, the wax could melt and the immature bees, called *larvae*, could die. Therefore, foraging worker bees collect water and place it in honey comb cells to be evaporated by fanning; thus, the colony has its own air conditioning system.

Unlike most cities, there is nearly perfect cooperation in a bee colony. There are no unions, no strikes, no political mud-slingings. They are all intensely patriotic and will defend with their life, against enemies. Its police force is the best in the world - not for regulating the members of the city, but to keep out the robbers, smugglers, and trespassers. Let one of these approach the gates of the city, and they will be attacked and subdued. Each citizen, except the males, is armed with one weapon, a sting. Their courage is never questioned and will attack, when provoked, any intruder regardless of size.

There is no mayor or city manager, city council, no political boss in this city. Though there is a queen, she does not direct the policies or the destiny. Nevertheless, in all the realm of nature, there is not a more efficient community.

Their system of dividing up jobs is one of the best in the world. Every worker knows her precise task and does it without being told or shown by a superior, for there is no superior.

In this bee city there is no unemployment problem. Nor is there old age pension. The bee city carefully regulates its working force to the seasons and the amount of work to be done. When depression or a bad season comes, the bee city reduces its population. When there is danger of the city starving, the control bees will dump the half-grown infants (bees in the larval form) out the city gate to perish. If any of the full grown youngsters are crippled, sick or not fully developed, they too, are removed from the city. In addition to all this, the old workers whose wings are worn out by toil are made to leave.

"What is the use," they say, "of raising a lot of babies and keeping a lot of old folks or cripples that can't work any more?" To feed the unborn and those that can't work might mean that all would starve. Every one works except the males (or drones) and even they are ruthlessly put out in the autumn so they will not deplete winter food stores.

Meet the Folks in Bee City

There are three distinctly different kinds of bees in each colony, namely the *queen*, which is the only perfectly developed female; the *drones*, which are the males; and the *workers*, which are *imperfect* females. They all go through the same stages of development: egg, larva (or grub), pupa (or chrysalis), and adult.

• The Queen

There is usually one queen per colony. Her sole duty is to lay eggs so the colony is continuously populated. She is in no sense the "boss or governor" of the hive.

Various colony activities are greatly influenced by the presence and condition of the queen. Her abdomen is larger than that of the worker bee but not so great in circumference

as that of the drone. Her entire body is considerably longer than that of the drone or worker, with wings in proportion to her size. She has a curved sting which she almost never uses, except against a rival queen.

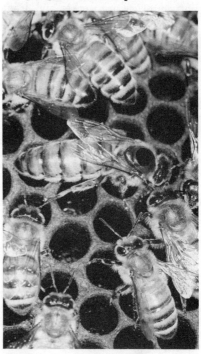

The queen's abdomen is long and slender and her thorax (back) is shiny black.

The queen comes from a **fertilized** egg, same as a worker bee. The worker bees themselves determine whether this egg shall develop into a queen or a worker.

Worker bees seem to instinctively sense a good queen. If she fails in fertility, is injured, lost or killed, they immediately prepare to rear another queen.

Raising Another Queen

Bees will raise a new queen when the old one is defective or missing, or to provide one when a swarm is soon to

33

issue. First, they build **queen cups,** located on the bottom edge of a comb. As the larva grows, the cell is enlarged until it takes the shape of a peanut. *Queen cells* (as they are called) project downward from the base, instead of horizontal, as are worker and drone cells.

This queen cell is still uncapped. You can see the large C-shaped queen larva floating on top of her food - royal jelly.

A queen larva is fed continuously with a diet of *royal jelly.* After the queen larva has been fed for five days on this special food, the workers seal the cell and the larva spins a **cocoon,** becoming a **pupa.** She remains in the pupal state for seven or eight days when a new queen will work her way out of the cell.

It ordinarily takes about sixteen days to develop a queen from the egg to the adult stage. When the workers are ready to have her come out, they assist by thinning the end of the queen cell. With her **mandibles,** a virgin queen completes the work of making the opening and then emerges. The new virgin roams over the combs for five or six days seeking

and destroying other virgin queens or queen cells that may be in the hive. She then takes her "nuptial" flights in the open air. She mates with 10 or more drones at this time. Once mated, which she does only once in her life, the queen can lay eggs for several years.

She very seldom leaves the hive again, unless to accompany a swarm. Within two or three days after mating, she begins laying eggs, thrusting her abdomen into an empty cell and neatly gluing an egg to the bottom of it. During the busy season of the year she is capable of laying over one thousand eggs daily. Her laying is regulated by the honey flow and the strength and needs of the colony.

There must be enough young workers to feed the larvae and incubate the eggs at a constant 95°F (34.6°C). She must lay many eggs in the summer, since the workers only live for six weeks. The population must reach over 40,000 individuals so there are enough bees to collect ample honey stores for winter survival. She can be the mother of 75,000 workers in one season, and as many as 500,000 offspring in her lifetime.

Only the Strongest

Normally there is one queen in a bee colony. Sometimes, queen mother and queen daughter may live peaceably together for some weeks but eventually the older queen disappears. This happens during supersedure (see Chapter 3).

Two sister queens, however, are natural enemies. Both unmated queens will fight to the death by stinging each other. This ensures that only the strongest will live to be the colony queen.

It is always good to remember that, as the queen is, so is the whole colony. Her blood is the blood of all the members of the hive, and the faults or virtues of her strain will be the faults or virtues of her progeny. So it is all important that the colony have a good queen.

The Queen's Choice

In the spring when many workers are needed, the queen lays the most eggs. But when the honey has been harvested in the fall, she lays fewer eggs. Her ordinary laying season is usually from February to October (in temperate regions.)

Perhaps the most wonderful of the special characteristics of the queen is her ability to lay *at will* either worker or drone eggs. She can do this because the **sperm cells** are contained in a sac known as the **spermatheca.** (These male cells are received from the drones during the mating flight.)

The eggs deposited in a worker-cell are fertilized. This means the queen releases some sperm while she lays an egg in a worker cell. From this egg, workers (or queens) are produced. Those eggs deposited in drone-cells are **unfertilized** (no sperm) and they produce drones.

Actually, the drone is a bee without a father. (An **infertile** queen can lay eggs, but these unfertilized eggs will produce drones.) This type of reproduction is known as **parthenogenesis,** and is possessed by only a very few other insects.

The queen may live for three or four years, laying all that time, the single mother of a half-million worker and drone bees. Ordinarily, a queen older than one year begins to fail and for this reason many beekeepers (and bees) replace their queens annually.

•The Drone

A drone, which is a male, has no father; but he always has a (**maternal**) grandfather. The queen bee lays an unfertilized egg to produce a drone - a case of parthenogenesis, or virgin birth. This means that the egg, which

Notice how the eyes of the drone touch at the top of his head. His body is chunky rather than slender.

was not fertilized, has only half the number of **chromosomes** as a worker or queen.

The drone's main function is to fertilize virgin queens. The wax cell in which he is reared is noticeably larger than those of worker bees. He has no organs for gathering nectar or secreting wax, no sting, and he does no work, living entirely on the toil of the workers. He is shorter and heavier than the queen, and larger and clumsier than the workers. His wings extend the whole length of his body, and his eyes are enormous. While he may help in heating the colony and in hive morale, most beekeepers try to limit drone population, which is neither necessary nor prudent.

Ten or more drones may mate with any one virgin, but none live to tell of it. As soon as they finish mating they die.

In the fall, workers drag out the drones. His presence is not tolerated in the winter months ahead, and he will soon perish.

Otherwise, he is a happy loafer, never working, always fed by others — hanging out with other drones at the corner **drone congregation area** (DCA). Here they wait in case a virgin queen flies by. If one is spotted, they all take off in hot pursuit. An interesting (and unexplained) fact is that drones use the SAME congregating areas year after year, even though all drones die each winter.

The drone does not live more than one summer season. At the close of the honey flow and mating season, he is not permitted to continue to be a burden to the colony. He is ruthlessly pushed out of the hive to perish.

• The Workers

As the name implies, workers do all the work: they collect, store and cure flower nectar to make honey, collect and store plant proteins or pollen, and secrete beeswax to make the honeycombs. They are also the guards, nurses, and cleaning crews to keep the colony running smoothly.

The worker bee (an **imperfect** female) is developed from a fertilized egg. In three days it hatches into a larva and is supplied with larval food by nurse bees. Eighteen days from the time the egg hatches, (twenty-one days from the time the egg was laid) the perfectly developed worker bee cuts through the capping and

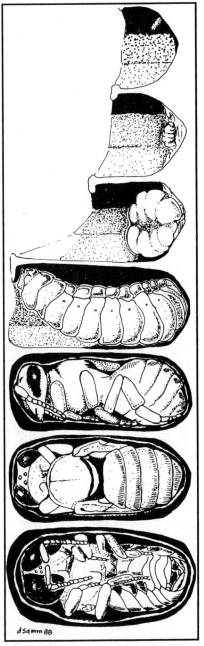

This diagram shows the stages of development a bee goes through. Egg, larvae and pupae are shown here. The bottom pupa is a drone.

struggles out. For some time she crawls unsteadily over the combs, is jostled about, and is apparently unnoticed by the other bees. She eventually finds a cell of honey and begins to feed.

Each job performed by a worker is regulated by her age. Her first job is to clean cells. Next she acts as nurse bee, taking care of larvae and secreting food, and helps to keep the brood warm. The young worker bee also helps feed and lick the queen, ventilate the hive, and aids in ripening the honey. She secretes wax and begins comb-building where it is needed.

After three weeks, her food and wax glands have dried out and she begins to move out of the warmer brood nest to hang out in the honey supers. Here she comes in contact with returning **foragers,** and soon she is gathering nectar and pollen.

Worker bees are the main work force of a colony. Compare their eye size with that of the drones. H. Doering Photo.

She is an armed defender of the colony and will die in her instinctive defense of it. Mature workers, sometimes called the "control bees," rule the colony, directing the queen's life and even driving out the drones when the honey flow is over.

Workers are the main force in a colony. They number around 50,000 or more in the summer, dropping to 30,000 or less during the winter. Workers born in the fall are different, physiologically, from those born in the spring. For one thing, they have more fat cells than spring workers. For another, they rarely leave the colony and do little foraging. For this reason, they usually live for 4 to 6 months. Their sisters born earlier, however, literally kill themselves with work, and live not more than six weeks.

It is ironic that the bees that gather the surplus crop of honey do not eat it, and the bees that eat it do not gather it.

•The Foragers

The older bees, called **field bees** or forager bees collect four things: water, nectar, pollen and propolis. They collect water to cool the hive and gather nectar from flowers, which they change into honey. A small cavity on each hind leg is used for storing and bringing in pollen also gathered from flowers. Pollen is an important food that is fed to the larva and is used as food for mature bees.

Propolis is gathered by workers from resinous buds, pine sap and other gummy substances, and is used as a varnish or glue. It cements things together and fills in cracks or uneven surfaces inside the hive.

Pollinating Machine

The worker bee is an efficient pollinating machine, perfected by thousands of years of evolution. By looking at the illustration, you can see that each part of the worker's body is geared to collect pollen and nectar.

Body hairs, including special hair combs and brushes help her to comb pollen grains adhering to her body. These are then packed into a special pollen press, which packs the grains together into a special pollen basket. In this way she can carry a large load back to the colony.

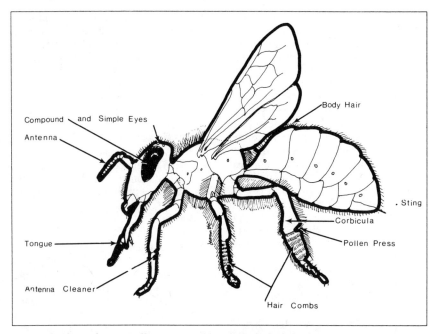

The worker honey bee is a pollinating machine, from the body hairs which comb, press and pack pollen, to the tongue and honey stomach for nectar.

The **antennae** serve as the scent and taste organs for bees, and are equipped with special hairs connected to nerves. In this way, she can smell and taste the different flowers she visits.

Her stomach is really an inflatable sack capable of expanding to carry drops of nectar. With her long tongue, she can reach into flower tubes to suck up this sweet liquid.

Truly, the honey bee is a marvelous creation.

Honey From Nectar

The sweet liquid found in flowers is not honey, but similar to sweetened water. It is called nectar. It is manufactured by the plant and secreted through special glands in the flower called **nectary glands**. Honey is the nectar of flowers, gathered, evaporated, and modified by bees.

Nectar is chemically the same as cane sugar, but when the bees store it in their combs and seal it over, it is converted into real honey, consisting of what is known as invert sugar. The sugar molecule is broken apart into the simple sugars known as **levulose** and **dextrose**. This means that the sugars can be directly absorbed in the human system without being changed.

The ring-shaped nectary from a sunflower floret. Notice the holes (called stoma) on the nectary wall and upper rim. D. Sammataro Photo.

Honey is similar to the sugars found in most fruits. It contains, besides levulose and dextrose, minute amounts of minerals such as iron, calcium, sodium, sulphur, magnesium, and phosphorus.

Refined cane sugar has none of these elements. If any of them were present originally, they would be lost in refining. Also, before cane sugar can be absorbed into the human body, it must be inverted by the digestive process into the kind of sugars found in honey.

one bee could gather enough nectar (four pounds) to make one pound of honey, it would have to make 80,000 trips of one mile each. This distance is equal to more than three times around the globe.

Bee Architects

Beeswax comes from special **wax glands** located underneath worker bees' abdomens. Once gorged with honey, young bees begin to secrete small wax chips. With their mandibles they chew, bend and shape the

Frames of capped honey, ready to be extracted.

Wax scales are secreted from 8 glands on the underside of a young worker.

How Many Miles Per Pound of Honey?

It takes about 20,000 bees to bring in a pound of nectar, which will make about one-fourth as much honey. It would, therefore, take 80,000 bees to bring in about four pounds of nectar, evaporate and modify it to equal a single pound of honey.

The average flying distance for a bee-load may be a mile and a half. If

chips into the familiar hexagonal (six-sided) honey comb shape. Hexagons have been studied by engineers for a long time, who have concluded that they are one of the strongest shapes used in construction. They provide more storage space than, say, circles, and also take the least amount of wax. This is good news since it takes seven pounds of honey for the bees to make one pound of wax.

5. Your First Honey Flow

As a beekeeper, you should study the plants in your locality to determine just when the major honey plants are blooming. When this happens, and bees will no longer feed from your sugar water, you can be assured that a *honey flow* is happening.

When more nectar comes in than is consumed, the surplus is cured and stored as honey. This is what beekeeping is all about.

What Is A Honey Flow?

Honey flows may be of major or minor consequence, depending which plants are blooming and on weather conditions. In the middle latitudes of the United States, spring, summer and fall seasons are marked by minor, major and minor flows in that order. But in other parts of the country, honey flows may occur continuously until winter.

While bees in a town or city may do very well on the scattered flowers in gardens, vacant lots and roadsides, it takes acres of honey plants to produce large quantities of surplus honey. For this reason bees are often kept in outyards, located on land surrounded by cultivated or native plants known to be important sources of nectar. In some instances, bees are moved to different locations during the season to take advantage of flowering plants which bloom at different times.

The spring season is marked by short, intense, though minor nectar flows. Fruit tree bloom and dandelions, for example, contribute enough fresh food to stimulate colony build-up. The peak strength of the colony usually coincides with the start of the mid-season or main honey flow. In the clover regions this is in June, July and perhaps August, if favorable weather and rainfall prolong the flowering period. Most of the surplus honey must be gathered during this major honey flow. Fall flows from goldenrod, asters, and other fall plants will often provide bees with substantial winter stores.

If these honey shallow supers are full, this beekeeper could harvest up to 270 pounds of honey! S. M. Thierman Photo.

If, despite all the right signs, the bees fail to fill frames with honey, the expected honey flow may have stopped because of drought, cold or hot weather. No matter how hard you try, bees cannot produce honey if there is no nectar out there. A mile or two shift in position of the apiary could make the difference between a good or bad crop.

Even if you have no choice of location, you will find that identifying the honey plants in your neighborhood will make beekeeping much more interesting. A survey of the local plants attractive to honey bees is the only way to determine the potential for beekeeping.

What Your Colony Should Look Like

Whether or not you began with a package, nuc or swarm, your preparations at this time should be the same.

If you began with a complete hive, your management practices will be a little different (see Chapter 9).

By summer, if you purchased your package in the spring, the bees should have the deep hive body almost full of brood and bees, with reserves of honey and pollen stored on the frames. If you do not see this, and you have been feeding them faithfully, your colony may have an inferior queen. At this time, the logic of buying more than one package is apparent - you may wish to join together your weaker colonies to form a larger unit or requeen your hive (see Chapter 9).

If your colony seems slow to start, it may be prudent not to harvest honey the first year, but wait until it is stronger. If you purchased an established hive, you should get a good crop of honey.

Perhaps your colony has already outgrown a single story, and you have already added a second deep super.

This may happen if you purchased a larger package, fed it and had good weather. If this is the case and the second story seems full, you should consider **supering** for honey.

Colony build-up is partly the result of good colony management. You'll need to provide good queens for the colony, practice swarm control, provide adequate brood and honey storage space and practice disease control. But all of these precautions will not make a honey flow.

Signs Of A Honey Flow

In the northern states east of the Mississippi River, the honey flow starts from the middle of June to the middle of July.

White burr comb between supers is a good indication of a strong honey flow. K. E. Farmer Photo.

When bees appear to be busy at the entrance, flying in and out, when the combs in the brood nest are white along the top edges and little spurs of wax are being built the bees are bringing in honey fast enough to need more room. Put on one or two supers at a time. If you wish, use a queen excluder at this time, placing it on top of the brood nest, under the supers.

Do not put on supers too soon. It retards the development of the colony if there is too much room to keep warm. The time to put on supers depends on the latitude and source of honey.

When the bees get well started in the first super and the flow is still going strong, another super may be put on top. Don't give the bees too much room all at once, or there will be some unfinished supers. The "chimney effect" happens when bees fill in only the center frames of each super.

When the first super is two-

(Above) A frame of uncapped honey, still mostly nectar, and fresh, white wax. (Below) A frame of fully capped honey, ready for the extractor. H. R. Stewart Photo.

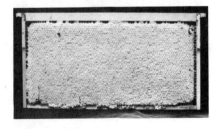

thirds capped over, it is ready to take off for extracting. Lift off all the supers and put the one that is next nearest full on top of the brood nest.

You can store the full super on top if you wish, if it is for extracted honey. Comb or **chunk honey** supers should be taken off at this time. Place full supers on top of an escape board. The

bees will go down through the escape. When bee-free, collect and process (see Chapter 7, Harvesting).

While we recommend the escape board as the least expensive way of clearing bees from supers, you can also shake or brush bees off each frame (see Chapter 7). If you are short of equipment, it is best to extract your supers as soon as possible, then you can return them to the bees to refill.

Equipment for Extracted Honey

Before the time arrives to super your bees, decide if you want **extracted** (liquid) honey or comb honey. Most beginners start with extracted honey. Whatever you choose, you will need to get some honey supers. These should be used *only* for honey. Using brood supers for honey production will discolor honey.

What Size Super?

There are several things to consider in selecting the best depth of super for you. For one thing, how much weight can you lift? Full depth hive bodies weigh 85-90 pounds when filled with honey. The medium super, when filled, weighs about 65 pounds and shallows weigh about 40 pounds.

An advantage of using the 3/4 or medium depth (6-5/8") super is that the same size can be used for brood and food chambers. (Usually one or two standard or deep hive bodies are used for brood chambers along with smaller honey supers.) There are advantages to having the brood and honey supers interchangeable. Of course, deep or standard hive bodies can also be used for supers, but there is the weight to consider.

In the North, two hive bodies are usually used to encourage the queen's egg laying and to store ample supplies

Four depths of supers are shown (L to R); comb or 1/2 depth, the 3/4, the shallow and the deep.

to carry the colony through the winter period. One deep is the brood chamber and the other is the food chamber; together they compose the **double story** hive. In the South, the brood chamber may be composed of only a deep hive body and a shallow or 3/4 depth super as a food chamber.

Many beekeepers prefer to use 2 deep brood chambers and the 3/4 depth or the shallow for honey.

Fortunately, the bees seem to adapt readily to any combination of super sizes, and to nearly any type of unit used as brood chambers. As long as the colony has ample room to expand the brood nest when needed, and ample space to store honey during the honey flow, any combination will do.

Make sure all frames used for extracting are wired and contain thick, wired foundation.

Other Equipment

Some other equipment will be needed for extracted honey. These include a queen excluder, extractor, and storage tank.

Queen excluders should be used for both extracted and comb honey production. Their purpose is to confine the queen to the broodnest when the honey flow is on, so she cannot get into the honey supers and start egg laying.

Besides the bee veil and smoker

Queen excluders are used to keep the queen from laying in the honey supers. To prevent drones from getting trapped, provide an upper entrance hole in the honey supers.

already described, you will need bee escapes and escape boards, and **uncapping knives.** (An electric uncapping knife will cost more but will uncap more rapidly).

A small honey extractor (centrifuge) will likewise be required. If you have only a few colonies, you can get by with a small 2-3 frame hand-powered extractor. But if you have 5 or more colonies, you may consider a larger, powered extractor.

In addition to all this, some kind of **container** will be needed to hold the **cappings.** You want the free honey to drain out of the cappings into the bottom of the tub, where it can be later drained off.

Look in the bee supply catalogs for uncapping pans, or visit some beekeepers and see what they recommend.

You will also need five gallon or other suitable containers to hold your **honey crop.** Five gallon round plastic buckets are commonly used for this.

If you plan to bottle honey, get a pail with a **honey gate** on it, to make bottling easier. If you expect more than 10 or 20 gallons, consider a

43

larger honey settling tank.

Honey storage and **settling tanks** are available in a variety of sizes, the most popular being 20, 45, and 100 gallons. The material from which they are made is heavy industrial grade plastic, stainless steel or galvanized iron. Since the chemical activity of honey causes it to react with some materials, honey tanks should be made of plastic, stainless steel, or galvanized metal that has been protected with a plastic-like sealer approved for food use. A tank holding 20 gallons (about 240 pounds) of honey, equipped with an outlet gate, can serve also as a **straining screen** holder, settling tank and a **bottling tank**.

When honey comes out of the extractor, it is full of debris that must be strained. A single thickness of closely woven strainer cloth can be stretched over the top of a holding tank and held firm by a cord or heavy rubber band around the rim. A better system is a cone-shaped metal strainer that fits over the tank top. The metal strainer supporting screen is available for the 45 and 100 gallon tanks from bee suppliers. Use a nylon type strainer to catch the debris. Cheese or other cloth strainers should be avoided since lint can be introduced into the honey.

A section of comb honey, fully capped, with fresh white wax.

market should be light in color. Amber and dark comb honey should be saved for home use or given to friends.

Comb Honey Equipment

If you are a beginner and decide to produce comb honey in wooden or plastic sections, you will *not* need a honey extractor, uncapping knife, uncapping or storage tank, or strainers for honey. All you need are comb honey supers, foundation, and sections.

Comb Honey

One of the most attractive foods is white-capped comb honey. The splendid reputation that honey has enjoyed throughout the ages as a delicious food has been from honey in the comb.

Well-filled **sections** of comb honey are from localities with a rapid honey flow of sufficient duration so the supers can be quickly filled. When comb honey remains on the hive too long, as in a slow honey flow, the cappings become discolored and the honey loses its attractive appearance.

Comb honey sold in the general

Section super or beeway super, holds 7 frames of 4 sections. Talk to other beekeepers if you need help to assemble this super.

KINDS OF SECTIONS. There are several sizes and kinds of sections. The wooden beeway section, 4-1/4" x 4-1/4" x 1-7/8", is the most commonly used. It is used in connection with a 4-5/8" **beeway super,** holding 28 comb sections. The split section, which is split on three sides, is easiest for the beginner since the foundation can be slipped in place. Plastic round sections are also available and are also

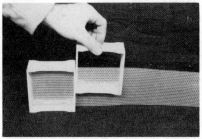

Thin foundation is always used for comb honey sections. The split section is easy to fill with foundation wax.

easy to assemble and use. They consist of special plastic frames and rings which split in the middle for foundation placement. Follow manufacturers instructions.

Colonies Should Be Strong at the Right Time

Since producing comb honey requires a large bee population, you should not try this on your package. It will not be ready for comb honey production unless it is *very* strong. Wait until the second summer. If you bought an established hive, go ahead and try it.

Management of the colonies for comb honey does not differ greatly from management for extracted honey, up to the time of putting on the supers. The problem in either case is to have the colonies reach their greatest strength just before or at the beginning of the main honey flow.

The important factors to remember in honey production are (1) young queens, together with an ample supply of honey and pollen for the winter and sufficient room for rearing the bees in the spring; (2) protection during the winter (by providing wind breaks, good top ventilation and packing); and (3) an abundance of honey and pollen during the spring.

It cannot be over-emphasized that only very strong colonies should

There are various round sections available, made up of plastic frames and rings. The thin foundation is placed in the inside and the frame snapped together.

A scale hive can tell you approximately what is happening in your apiary — honey flow, dearth or a weak or strong colony. J. McCreary Photo.

be used for the production of comb honey.

When to Put on Comb Honey Supers

Beginners often put comb honey supers on too soon, before the honey flow starts, or when the colonies are too weak. For bees to do their best work, it is necessary to have a rapid and strong honey flow, and enough bees to crowd into a deep super.

Watch carefully when the first blossoms of major honey plants in your area bloom. If the main source is white or sweet clover, then the first honey in the states north of the Ohio and east of the Mississippi Rivers may be expected during June and July. In Florida and California the main honey flow is between March and May. Talk to beekeepers in your area as to when to expect the major honey flow.

Another tool you can use is a hive scale. Rapid gains in your scale hive over a few days could indicate a strong flow is coming in.

When the plants are well in bloom, the bees are flying in and out of the hives, and the combs near the top are whitened, you can put on the first comb honey super.

Preparing Your Hive for Comb Honey

Fill one deep story with emerging brood and remove the second deep to a weaker hive. Some beekeepers place a shallow super full of honey on top of the brood nest to provide ample honey stores. Now place a queen excluder on top, then put on your comb honey supers. There are many techniques for supering for comb honey. We suggest you read several books and talk with experienced beekeepers before beginning.

If after about a week the bees don't go up, it may help a little to put in some "bait" sections. These are sections that were partly filled from the previous year. Place this bait frame into the center of the comb honey super. The bees should soon go up.

If the honey flow is strong, additional supers should be given as fast as the bees will occupy them and draw out the foundation uniformly. If the bees fill the entire super and are found working in every section, a new super should be placed on top of the excluder. Remove finished supers quickly to keep cappings white. This process is repeated as fast as the bees occupy the new super and are working in all of the sections. On the other hand, if the bees work only in the middle of the super, neglecting the end frames, they do not need more room.

PROBLEMS IN COMB HONEY PRODUCTION. In locali-

A slatted rack is placed on top of the bottom board, under the first brood super. It provides better ventilation and clustering space.

ties where the **swarming season** occurs during the main honey flow, reducing two story colonies to a single story and supering for comb honey may cause the bees to swarm. At this critical time, the bees must be induced to enter the supers promptly and begin work there, to prevent crowding the brood nest.

Open the entrance all the way to its full summer size. If very hot, shade the hives from the direct rays of the sun. Some beekeepers use special ventilation bottom board racks or covers to allow maximum air flow. The hives may also be painted white or another light color. If the colonies can be carried over the critical period after giving the first comb honey supers, the battle against swarming is often won.

Experience is the best teacher. Talk with local comb honey producers to learn their techniques and keep on trying.

Remember, not all localities are adapted to produce comb honey. For best results, the honey flow must be exceptionally good - coming in with a rush so the sections may be filled and removed quickly to minimize **travel stains.**

Not all beekeepers have the time or experience needed to produce comb honey. It requires careful attention to prevent swarming. Unless the bees are crowded, forcing them to fill out and work these small supers, too many unfinished sections will result.

6. Honey Plants and Pollination

While it is not the scope of this book to list all the possible honey plants in your area, you should be aware of the more common ones. There are several books available that list both major and minor honey plants in North America.

If you are interested in learning what plants your bees forage on for nectar and pollen, simply walk around the proximity of your bee yards and take notes. Trees, shrubs, crops, wild and ornamental plants all offer food for bees from early spring to late fall. Be sure to place your bees in the best possible location that can take advantage of all the plants throughout the bee season.

In general, the major honey crop is secured in mid-season when the clovers and alfalfa bloom. Some regions have special flows from locally abundant nectar sources. The plant species that are known for producing enough nectar for surplus honey, include: alfalfa, aster, basswood, black mangrove, buckwheat, citrus, clovers (sweet, white and alsike), cotton, fireweed, gallberry, goldenrod, sage, saw palmetto, sourwood, soybeans, spanish needles and tupelo.

Agricultural Crops

The USDA lists the following crops which are dependent on insect pollinators to produce seed or fruit. See how many different ones you eat in a day:

Basswood or Linden trees (Tilia spp) produce ample nectar that makes an exceptionally good honey. A. Mullin Photo.

alfalfa	currant
almond	dewberry
apple	eggplant
avocado	garlic
blackberry	gooseberry
blueberry	herbs &
buckwheat	spices
cacao	huckleberry
cardamon	kola nut
cashew	litchi
chayote	macadamia
cherry	melons and
cinnamon	squash
citrus fruit	mustard
clovers	onion & leek
cole crops	passion fruit
cranberry	peaches &
cucumber	nectarines

pears	tung
persimmon	turnip
pimento	vegetable
plums	seeds
quinine	-artichoke
radish	-asparagus
raspberry	-caraway
rutabaga	-celery
sapote	-chive
sunflower	vetch (hairy)
sweetclover	watermelon
tea	

Alsike clover is another good source of pollen and nectar. A. Mullin Photo.

Bees working the female flower of a pumpkin. Pollen grains adhering to their body hairs fertilize the flower while they collect the nectar.

This list does not include flowering ornamentals. Many seed companies depend on bees to pollinate plants so they can sell us cosmos or marigold seeds each spring. Moreover, the clovers and alfalfa on the list above not only feed our livestock (so add meat, butter and milk products), but are important soil fertilizers. The latest figures on the value of these crops dependent upon and benefited by honey bees, are in the millions of dollars annually.

Pollination

Pollination is simply the transfer of pollen or sperm cells from the **anther** (male part) of a flower to the **stigma** (female part). If the transfer takes place on the same blossom, or on another blossom on the same plant, it is called **self-pollination.** Beans for example, are self pollinated, since each flower is capable of transferring its own pollen.

Cross-pollination, on the other hand, happens when the pollen of, say a Delicious apple is carried to the stigma of a Macintosh apple. Apples and other fruits are also an example of a **self-sterile** plant; that is why you never see an orchard of only Delicious

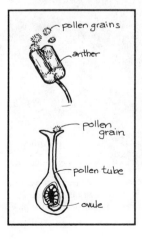

Pollen grains, originated in the flower's anther. They land on the stigma, grow a root or tube, and deposit the sperm cells in the ovule to form a seed.

49

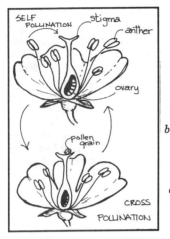

Self-pollination is common in beans but cross-pollination is needed, especially for many fruit crops.

some plants are **wind pollinated**. This means that the male flower produces large quantities of light pollen which is carried by the wind and eventually lands on the female flower. Pine trees and other evergreens are good examples, as are grasses, (and their cultivated cousins corn, oats and wheat) and our favorite, ragweed.

Some people have an allergic reaction to pollens of this type. We say they have **hayfever**, but it really means their bodies are reacting to airborne pollen grains.

But let's get back to the cucumber. Each plant in this large family, which includes pumpkins, melons and squash, produce both male and female flowers on the same vine. How does the pollen get from one to another? If you said with the help of a honey bee, you were right. Most growers know this, and rent hives of bees just when their pumpkin patch is blooming, so the bees can produce lots of Jack'o-lanterns and pumpkin pies for you.

apple trees — they would never set fruit.

What does the honey bee have to do with all this? Many plants, like apples, or cucumbers cannot pollinate their own blossoms. It is true that

What is Pollen?

Pollen grains carry the sperm or male cells that will eventually unite with a female **ovule,** to form a seed. Although these pollen grains may look like red, yellow, orange or green powder to you, under a microscope, the small grains take on a particular shape. Each plant species has its own shape of pollen. This is how plant archaeologists, (or *paleo-botanists*), can name plant species from mud samples buried in lakes. Because of their special tough outer coat, pollen grains have been recorded as old as 10,000 years!

When a bee visits a male flower of our friend the cucumber plant, she sticks in her head to lap up some of the nectar. In doing this, she rubs against the anthers and gets a lot of pollen grains sticking to her hair. When she

Bee hives in orchards are a common and necessary sight. They are often moved off after the trees have finished blooming. J. A. Happ Photo.

leaves the flower, she hovers briefly and combs her body to brush the pollen into compact pellets which adhere to her hind legs. Then she repeats this with each flower, getting more and more pollen on her body.

One cucumber, such as this one, requires at least 20 visits by honey bees to fertilize it properly.

Eventually, she lands on a female flower which has no pollen, but offers a larger quantity of nectar. In order to reach this sweet reward, however, she must push past the large stigma. While doing this, loose pollen grains on her body stick to the moist tip of the stigma, and the flower has been pollinated. But one trip is not sufficient. If you cut open a cucumber, you see there are lots of seeds. Researchers estimate that it takes about *20 visits* by bees to adequately pollinate *one* cucumber. If the bee doesn't do it, then people must be hired to act like a bee; and if that happens, the price of ONE cucumber could be as high as $10.00.

How Does the Pollen Fertilize the Egg?

Once the pollen is attached to the stigma, an incredible thing happens. The pollen grain starts to grow a root! This root, called a **pollen tube**, contains the sperm cells needed to fertilize the ovule, or embryo seed, in the ovary. The pollen tube grows down the stigmatic tissue and into the ovary. Once it has found an unfertilized ovule, the two sperm cells (contained in the pollen tube) are released. One cell fuses with the egg nucleus which turns into the seed.

A single pollen grain growing its tube into the stigma of a sunflower floret. D. Sammataro Photo.

The other sperm cell goes to the center of the ovule and unites with the polar nuclei; this becomes the endosperm which turns into the first two leaves of a seedling (or cotyledons). From this complex action, most plants on earth arise!

A forager bee returns to the colony with her pollen baskets full. She will scrape them off into an empty cell. H. Doering Photo.

Pollen As Food

Pollen contains a number of nutrients, like **carbohydrates**, proteins and minerals. The composition varies according to the plant species, and bees who collect pollen are unable to distinguish the more nutritious ones. Pollen is the protein source for honey bees, since they are entirely vegetarian; it contains between 10 and 35% protein. Vitamins are also present, including A, C, D, E, B_1, B_2, B_6 and B_{12}. There are also the minerals sulfur, nitrogen, phosphorus and many minor elements, amino acids, sugars, oils and enzymes.

After a bee collects pollen in her **leg baskets**, these pellets are stored in the comb cells back at the hive. House bees pack many pellets in one cell and then seal it with a little honey and wax; it is then called **bee bread**. This substance is a necessary part of the diet of both adult and immature bees, and a colony collects more than 100 pounds each season. It is calculated that 120 mg of pollen is needed to rear one bee from egg to adult. Furthermore, the nurse bees, who feed the queen and other larvae with royal jelly, require pollen to stimulate their brood-food glands.

This is especially important in late winter as the queen starts to lay eggs in January and February. Since bees cannot forage for pollen during this time of year, there must be ample bee bread stores for them. If this is not available, it must be provided.

Many beekeepers purchase pollen substitutes, which contain yeasts, flours and sugars, specifically designed for this purpose. But the best food of all is natural pollen.

Pollen For Human Use

Pollen is routinely sold for human consumption. While some claim that pollen is a superior food, with curative powers, authoritative reports are contradictory. Some researchers assure us the hard outer coat of the pollen grain cannot be digested by humans. Remember, pollen grains have survived for thousands of years. Whatever the claims, there is a market for it, which may be lucrative for beekeepers.

A word of warning should be injected here. Some people may be **hypersensitive** to pollen resulting in an **allergic reaction**. Furthermore, some pollens may contain **insecticide** poisons, since beekeepers may trap contaminated pollen before it can kill their bees. Know the source of the pollen before you buy (see Chapter 7; *Pollen as a Crop*).

7. Harvesting

Your bees have now produced supers full of capped honey and you are saying to yourself; "How do I harvest it?" Whether or not you have supers of comb honey or extracting frames, you must first separate the bees from their honey. Here are some ways to do it.

Bee Brush: If you have only a few supers to take off, and the bees are still actively foraging, a **bee brush** can be used. Take off the super of extracting or cut comb honey. Have an empty super handy that you can cover with an extra outer cover. One by one, gently brush bees from each frame; bees should be brushed at the hive entrance. As you finish a frame, place it in the empty super and cover it to prevent **robbing.**

Escape Boards: There are several types of escape boards. The **screened ventilated** (or **moving board**) and the regular inner cover can both be fitted with a **Porter bee escape.** (This is the one with a one-way exit through which bees pass.) Two or more supers stacked above these boards fitted with bee escapes can be free of bees in 24-48 hours. Make sure there are no cracks or holes in the honey supers, or robbing bees will get in. The **Conical escape** board has cone-shaped bee escapes rather than Porter escapes, and is used the same way. They are sometimes faster, since there is more than one exit for the bees.

Fume Board: If you have many supers to take off and only a few days to do it in, you may want to consider a **fume board.** A sheet of tin covers absorbent cloth which has been

A screened ventilated moving board, fitted with a porter bee escape, becomes an escape board.

A conical escape board has many exits for bees and may work a little faster. This is the bottom.

sprinkled with a chemical like **Bee Go**. The fume board is placed on top of the honey supers for a few minutes; the bees are repelled by the fumes and are driven down into the brood nest. Cleared supers are then removed and covered.

Bee blowers are also used by commercial beekeepers, but it requires two people for efficient use of time, and the queen could be blown out and lost.

Preparing to Extract Supers

Once you have your supers inside your **honey house,** the fun part (albeit a little sticky) can begin. To make your extracting easier, follow some simple rules: Store your honey in a warmed honey house, since warm combs extract faster than cold ones. Examine each comb quickly and do not extract it if it contains brood, more than half uncapped honey, or if it is broken. This is now a good time to clean frames of burr comb and propolis, and to cull those frames which are broken or contain dark, old or crooked combs.

Now get the extraction equipment together that you need: a tool to cut off the cappings that hold the honey in the cells, a container to put those cappings in, a container that will allow the honey to drip (or spin) out, something to strain the honey, a container that allows you to bottle it, bottles, and labels.

To cut off the cappings, a simple serrated knife works well if you have only a few supers to uncap. A **capping scratcher** can also be used. Heated and electric knives speed the operation for those with many supers, and the steam heated uncapping machine lets you have both hands for the operation.

Cutting the Cappings

If honey supers are removed from the hive during warm weather, they can be extracted and the honey strained without the use of supplementary heat. If not, store supers in a warm room (90-95°F, 32-35°C) for 24 hours, to facilitate honey extracting and handling.

In cool weather, storing the supers this way will be needed, to warm them up for easier extraction. Or you can warm them by placing an electric light bulb (75 to 100 watts) underneath a stack of supers and leaving it overnight. Place the bulb, in a socket fastened to a base, in an empty super shell at the bottom of a stack of about five supers. Another method of warming is to fan warm air over the stack of staggered supers; allow the moving air to circulate across the tops of the frames. This also helps cure (dehy-

A steam-heated or electric uncapping knife quickly cuts away the wax cappings covering the honey.

Various knives used to uncap honey range from the serrated, water heated, electrical and steam-heated.

drate) unripened honey.

To uncap, pick up a frame and place it on end so that the center of the bottom end bar rests upon the nail above an **uncapping tank** (see illus.).

Uncapping knives (have more than one) can be heated in a can of hot water, or you can use electric knives. With an upward sawing movement, slice off the cappings, dropping them into the uncapping tank. The movement of the knife should be upward, with the combs leaning so the cappings will fall clear of the comb and

This small plastic uncapping tank is ideal for hobbyist beekeepers.

into the tank. The other side of the comb is uncapped the same way. The knife is wiped off and put back into the hot water. Another comb is picked up and uncapped with the other hot knife. Some tanks are large enough to

store 8-10 uncapped frames to drip until they are ready for the extractor. If not, place uncapped frames immediately into the extractor to drip.

Extracting

After all the combs have been uncapped they are ready for the extractor. Equalize the frames around

Radial extractors spin out both sides of the frame at the same time. Below is a cutaway of the frames in position.

the extractor to keep the reel in balance. If you are using a **radial extractor**, start spinning slowly, to even up the load, then go up to full speed until no more honey comes out.

Basket type extractors will only spin out one side at a time. They are usually hand cranked and are good for small time hobbyists.

If you have a **basket type extractor**, balance the load and start slowly spinning until one-half the honey is out on the first side. The combs should now be reversed and put back in their respective pockets to extract the other side. Speed up the extractor until the second side is clean of honey. Reverse again and spin at full speed until the first side is clean. Be careful not to whirl the extractor too fast or you will break the combs.

As soon as they are extracted, put the frames into empty supers. Place empty supers near the extractor, on top of heavy paper, newspaper or plastic sheeting. This lets the combs drip on the paper and not on your floor. This is a messy job, so wear a work apron or coverall that can be easily washed. Be sure to drain the honey from the extractor after every spin. A 5 gallon plastic pail is good for this.

Two types of honey storage tanks. The one above is plastic while the one on the right is stainless steel. Both can be fitted with a honey gate.

Straining and Settling Honey

After extracting, honey is poured into a storage tank, fitted with a strainer. If the honey is warm, it is much easier to strain. Allow it to remain in the storage tank for at least 24 hours; most of the air bubbles and the fine particles of wax and other extraneous material will rise to the surface and can later be skimmed off. Honey drawn off the bottom of the tank will be fairly clear.

Honey varies considerably in its tendency to **granulate**. It depends largely upon the flowers from which the nectar is taken. If the honey is for home use or is sold directly to the consumer, it may be bottled straight from the settling tank without heating. If, however, the honey is to remain on a grocery shelf or otherwise stored in bottles, process it with heat to avoid crystallization in the jar. Honey to be sold as **natural** or **raw** calls for a minimum of straining, and little or no heat.

If honey is not bottled immediately after extracting, it should be drawn out of the storage tank into 5 gallon pails or 55 gallon drums. Heating and bottling honey is discussed in Chapter 10, *Marketing Your Honey* .

•After Extracting

After extracting, the supers should be put back on the hives for the bees to clean up. Make sure none of these wet supers are from diseased colonies, since you could quickly spread disease throughout your apiary. It is best to distribute these wet supers on several hives, rather than all on one. Put them out late afternoon to keep robbing under control (see Chapter 9, *Robbing*).

At the end of the day's extracting, there will be cappings and honey in the uncapping tank. Let the honey drip overnight and the next day drain the tank. The honey can be strained

and bottled, but it may be damaged if you used an electric uncapping knife. Scorched honey is not good to eat, but can be fed back to a weak hive. Some extractors are specially adapted to spin out cappings. Other beekeepers let the bees clean them out or melt them in boiling water, honey and all, to collect the valuable cappings wax.

When through with the work of extracting, wash out the extractor with cool water — hot water will melt wax which will later harden.

Comb and Cut Comb Honey Harvesting

Taking Off Comb Honey

The sooner comb honey sections are taken off after they are filled, the whiter the cappings will be. As a rule, it is best not to wait until every section in a super has been finished. Usually, the super should be taken off as soon as all, except the sections in the outer rows, are finished.

It is easier to free supers of comb

Section comb honey is generally shipped in some kind of container to protect it from dust and handling. Each box should show the packer or producer's name, address and the net weight.

honey from bees by using escape boards. Place it under the finished super, taking care that the cover fits tight and no bees can enter the super from the outside. The next day the super is usually free of bees and can be removed. The unfinished sections from several supers can be stored and then assembled in an empty super and given back to the bees to finish.

The finished supers of comb honey should be stacked in tight piles in a warm, dry room of your honey house. You can store them like this for only 8 or 10 days. Otherwise the **wax moth** can get in and ruin the combs. It is best to sort and freeze comb honey sections as soon as possible.

The propolis on the edges of the sections should be first scraped off. Then sort the sections by weight, color of cappings (white or tan), and color of honey.

In many states the law requires that the net weight of honey sections be stamped on every box or container. This is also required for all comb honey that is shipped across a state line on its way to market, since it then comes under the rules of the Federal Government.

Wrap each section in a plastic or cellophane wrapper or place it in a window carton or plastic box. In this way, the honey is protected from dust and insects, and presents a more attractive appearance on the grocer's shelves.

Producing Chunk and Cut Comb Honey

Chunk honey is a section of comb honey, cut from a frame, and placed in a honey jar. Liquid honey is then poured in to fill the jar. Preparing chunk honey for market requires some care and skill. The requirements needed to produce chunk comb honey are basically the same as for comb honey, only the super outfitting is different. Cut comb honey is actu-

Chunk comb honey is packed in a jar then filled with liquid honey.

ally squares of honey cut from the frame and wrapped individually, instead of being placed in a bottle with liquid honey.

For chunk and cut comb honey, use 8 or 9 frames with **unwired foundation** in shallow section honey supers. Use the thinnest foundation available. As with section comb honey, delicacy and freshness of the comb are vitally important.

Used frames must be scrubbed and cleaned of any accumulation of wax or propolis. A boiling bath of detergent and water is also recommended. Another kind of frame, with a grooved top bar and solid bottom bar is also available for cut comb honey.

Various devices for fastening the foundation in these frames have been devised. Usually, a **wax tube fastener** is used. It is a hollow metal tube fitted with a wooden handle. The applicator can feed a steady flow of hot wax through the point along the edge of the sheet of foundation, securing it top and bottom to the frame.

As with comb honey, use your strongest colonies for cut comb or chunk honey. A strong work force is needed to quickly draw out foundation into clear, straight combs.

A strong colony, crowded with bees, is required to produce comb honey quickly, so the cappings don't get stained.

Place prepared chunk honey supers above a queen excluder when fresh nectar starts to come in from the major nectar source. As soon as the combs are filled and partially capped, another super may be added. To preserve the white cappings, remove finished supers as soon as they are 3/4 capped over. Keep giving supers until the flow slows down.

•Packaging Chunk or Cut Comb Honey

Cutting the finished comb from the frame is a fairly easy process. A heated knife blade helps make a clean cut. Place the frame on a wire screen, over a tank. Cut the comb free of the frame and lift off wooden part. Now cut the comb to fit the containers in which you are packing them.

This comb honey can either be drained and put into containers (plastic bags or trays) or made into chunk honey. Chunk comb honey can also be cut to fit into a wide-mouthed glass

Cut frames of honey for chunk comb over a screen, allow them to drip, then pack in wide-mouthed jars and fill with honey.

Cut comb honey is allowed to drain over-night, then packaged in attractive cartons. These are small 'sampler' sized boxes.

container. The empty spaces are filled with clear liquid honey to make an attractive pack. This is excellent for either home use or the market. Light grades of cut comb, packed in a light liquid honey give the best appearance. Any off-color or partially filled comb should be mashed and allowed to drip. It can be bottled later as extracted honey.

Round Sections

Plastic **round sections** are very easy to prepare for market. They require only a little scraping and trim-

All this round section needs is to trim off the excess foundation, then cover it with round plastic covers. The label goes around the outside edge.

ming of the excess foundation. You can purchase plastic lids to fit top and bottom and a special label to go around the outside. Their only drawback is the initial expense and the fact that you cannot re-use the inner rings.

Beeswax

Young bees between 12 and 18 days old have active wax glands on the underside of their abdomens. When amply fed with pollen and gorged with honey or syrup, these glands manufacture droplets of liquid wax which harden on contact with air. This hardened drop is called a *wax scale* which the bees chew to soften and mold into honey comb. Bees engaged in secreting wax and building comb are **festooning.**

Bees festooning in this manner are secreting wax to make a honey comb. A. W. Wittekindt Photo.

Not only are you able to harvest honey from your bees, but you also get valuable beeswax. Throughout the year, collect burr comb scrapings, old combs and broken pieces of foundation and melt them in a **solar wax** or **electric melter.** When you uncap frames during honey extraction, save those cappings, since they melt down into some of the finest wax.

Scrape off this valuable burr comb and melt it down for it's wax.

You can sell cleaned (by boiling) wax chunks as is, to neighbors, friends or at roadside stands, but a more attractive alternative is to make them into candles or other decorations. Craft and hobby shops have books and wax molds. You can trade wax in at some bee dealers for cash, foundation, or beekeeping equipment. Whatever you do, don't throw it away.

Beeswax:
Preparing a Quality Product

Beeswax is a valuable commodity and can be ruined by improper handling and extraction. This versatile and non-perishable material has many home and commercial uses, including candy, cosmetics, dental and medicinal preparations, floor pastes, polishes, leather or metal preparations, candles and textile dying. It cannot be synthetically reproduced, is hypo-allergenic and its properties of plasticity and low melting point (143-151°F; 62-66°C) make it a highly prized product.

Because of its complex nature, beeswax can be easily damaged if heated to excess or stored improperly.

There are some simple rules to follow before beginning: 1) WAX IS VERY FLAMMABLE. Never heat wax directly over open fire. Melt wax in a double boiler (over water) over the fire; 2) Metal containers such as iron, zinc, brass and copper may discolor wax. Use aluminum, tin or stainless steel for best results; 3) Honey and wax should be separated as soon as possible since fermenting honey can ruin wax; and 4) Don't store dark, old honey combs for a long time — this encourages the destructive behavior of wax moths.

Harvesting Wax — The easiest method of collecting wax is while you are harvesting honey. As soon as possible after harvesting, you should separate wax and honey.

After draining, soak the cappings in rainwater for a few hours to rinse

out the honey; this water can later be made into honey vinegar. Then melt the wax; a solar wax melter is good for cappings. (Honey that is heated when wax is extracted, such as in a solar wax extractor, is not good to eat or sell; it is not even very good as bee food).

Rendering Old Comb — There are many simple methods of melting wax. Before you begin, separate dark combs from lighter wax cappings or new combs. Darker wax is less valuable and will darken lighter wax.

Once the wax has been separated, it can now be made into cakes. Melt these old combs in clean rainwater (equal proportions) over slow heat until it is just melted. Overheating wax will darken it more and decompose its structure. Once it is melted, skim wax off and strain it through a clean cloth (to trap pollen, honey and propolis) into a clean container. Soap the container lightly to facilitate removing the hardened

Beeswax can be made into candles or sold as blocks. It is mostly used in cosmetics, pastes and waxes.

cake. Remove the covered container to a draft-free room to cool slowly. Dust should not get into it. When completely hard (24 hrs.), shake out the cake and scrape off any dark particles from the bottom.

A more efficient way to melt old combs is to press the combs in a steam or hot water press. Whether using a screw or lever press, they are much more efficient for large quantities of wax. Combs are wrapped in cloth bags and placed in the press.

The remaining waste product, called **slumgum,** has been used as smoker fuel and a soil builder. As a smoker fuel, a small chunk is placed on top of the regular fuel to keep it from going out. If used for soil improvement, it should be first composted or allowed to decompose with dirt, manure and green leaves. Once softened, work into your gardens, especially where the soil is hard or too sandy.

Pollen As A Crop

Pollen is not only important as a food source for bees, but can be collected and sold for human consumption. Pollen, in recent years, has gained a market value as a human food and can be an interesting and potentially profitable activity for beekeepers who are willing to take the time to understand proper trapping, cleaning and marketing methods.

•Trapping Pollen

A **pollen trap** is simply a wire screen set up so when returning bees enter the colony loaded with pollen pellets, they must squeeze through the screen mesh. Since the pellets are rather bulky, they are scraped off the legs of the bees, and fall below into a collecting tray. This does not hurt the bees, but slows them down coming or leaving the hive. There are basically two types of traps; those that fit in the hive entrance or in a special entrance hole, and those that fit on the hive bottom board. The latter tends to collect hive debris as well, so are not recommended for commercial use.

The trap, regardless of the design, must have a drone escape, (since they do not fit through the screen), and should be easy to deactivate (screen removed). In dry climates, trapped pollen may be collected weekly, but in more humid weather,

This pollen trap fits in an auger hole in the super. You must first train the bees to enter this hole, then put the trap in place.

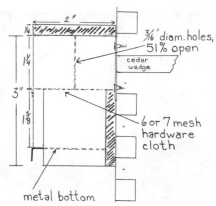

pollen pellets can easily mold if not collected daily.

It is inadvisable to leave the trap set for more that a few days each week. Set a routine where you trap, say on Friday and Saturday and collect on Sunday, and leave it open the rest of the week. Since bees also require pollen for their normal growth and development, it may cause unreasonable stress to continually rob them of it. Trap from your strongest colonies, since weaker ones will not only bring in less pollen, but may die as a result. The affect of pollen trapping varies from lowering brood rearing to increased honey storage. Experiment with a few of your own hives before going into this in a big way.

•Curing Pollen

Freshly collected pollen should be cleaned of debris, dried or frozen as soon as possible; this preserves its nutritional value. Here are some tips:

1. Dry in a warm room, oven or good dryer as long as the temperature is kept between 95 and 97°F (35-36°C). Properly dried pellets should not stick together. Once dried, seal in airtight containers; pollen dried in this way should be good for a year or so. Freeze pollen 24-48 hours to kill pests or pest eggs.

2. Keeping fresh pollen frozen in paper or plastic bags at 0°F (-18°C). This will last several years, but must be used immediately or dried.

To feed pollen back to bees, pour some around the hole in the inner cover, mix with syrup to form a paste or sprinkle some in empty combs. A word of warning here - pollen may contain **chalkbrood** spores. If you are buying pollen pellets as bee food, know the source of that pollen. If there is no chalkbrood in your area, consider buying a pollen substitute, or trap your own pollen, rather than risk getting chalkbrood (see Chapter 11, *Pests & Diseases*).

•Packing Pollen

Some beekeepers find ready markets for pollen, as is. Others pulverize it and put it in tablets or capsules. There are no label requirements yet, but it seems appropriate to label jars of pollen pellets as you would honey: name, address, zip and phone of beekeeper, plant source, if known, and net weight. A warning for allergic persons might be in order as well. Of course, collecting, processing and marketing pollen is labor intensive, perhaps more so than honey production. Converting colonies from honey to pollen production should be carefully considered. Start slowly, and observe the affect it has on your bees.

To keep pollen from molding, collect it every day, and then dry and freeze it. USDA photo.

8. Spring and Summer Management

Record Keeping

It is important to keep records of anything you work with — dairy cows, vegetable garden activities or beehives. Since each hive is a unique entity, a diary of their progress or failures will help you determine the potential for it. If a particular queen is exceptionally good, you may want to requeen all your hives with her progeny. You won't know that if you don't keep records.

Number or otherwise mark, each hive in each apiary, and keep a running account. Some beekeepers attach cards on each hive, write on the outer cover, or merely keep a diary of each apiary. Whatever you do, here are some points to record:

- dead colonies
- disease problems
- medication date(s)
- color and temperament of queen/colony
- industry

Record keeping is an important part of beekeeping.

- honey removed (# of supers) and dates
- propolizing tendencies
- winter hardiness
- swarms issued
- disease resistance
- cleanliness (bottom board clean or littered)
- brood pattern (compact or loose)
- handling ease
- whiteness of wax cappings (save white ones for comb honey)
- conservation of stores

Other records you need to keep for tax purposes are:
- mileage to apiary
- equipment bought, destroyed, sold or stolen
- dates of purchases: queen(s), bees, equipment, medication
- pesticide losses
- medication (for you - bee sting therapy)
- lectures, talks or fairs attended
- books or conference fees
- equipment for selling and extracting honey (labels, bottles)
- amount of honey sold (comb honey or extracted)
- pollination fees collected
- amount of wax or other hive products sold

Requeening Your Colony

A common cause of package failure is the loss or supersedure of the package queen. If the queen is lost, and the bees have no larvae from which to raise a new one, then you must either join the queenless colony with a queenright one, or you must introduce a new one.

Introducing a New Queen

A strange or new queen will be attacked by queenless bees. Therefore, queens should be introduced

A good queen should lay many eggs (see eggs in cells) to produce a lot of workers. If not, requeen your colony.

soon after the colony becomes queenless, within the first few hours if possible. If you wish to replace an old or defective queen (one that continues to lay few eggs and places them irregularly), this queen should not be removed until the new one arrives. The dequeening and requeening may be accomplished at the same operation.

Feeding syrup (to simulate a honey flow) before, during and after queen introduction will facilitate her acceptance. A frame of capped brood and larvae taken from a stronger colony, will supply the young bees required to feed the new queen and her larvae.

Whenever you put in a new queen, and the bees cling so tightly to the wire of the queen cage that it is difficult to brush them off, it may be difficult or impossible to introduce her. This means that these bees probably have a "queen" and will not accept any other, even after five or six days in the cage. You should then give this colony a frame of eggs or young larvae.

If such a colony is queenless, the

bees will start queen cells. If no queen-cells are found, there is either a virgin queen or **laying workers** present (see *Laying Workers*).

•How to Introduce A Queen

There are a number of good methods to introduce queens. If there are queen cells started you do not wish to hatch into a new queen, remove them first. When your new queen arrives, bore a hole through the candy by poking a hole in it with a nail. Place the cage, screen side down, above the opening between two frames in the center of the super, so the bees can easily get to it.

If the inner cover of the hive has no rim and cannot be inverted to provide space for laying the queen cage on top, insert the cage between two frames, leaving space so the wire cloth is uncovered. This will crowd the frames together on each side, but you can remove an outside frame to make room, or it can be readjusted when the queen-cage is removed. In about 24-48 hours, the bees will have gnawed away the candy in the cage and released the queen. The colony should

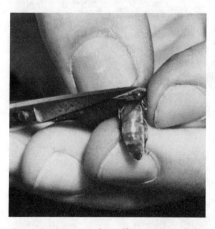

Some beekeepers clip off one wing of the queen for identification or to keep her from leaving with a swarm. USDA Forsythe Photo.

be left undisturbed for at least five days after the queen has been accepted, for opening the hive soon after introducing may result in the loss of the queen by "balling" (see below).

If the queen has not been released after 5 days, and the bees seem to accept her, spray her with syrup, pull off the screen and drop her down between the frames.

If the queen is not marked, dab a bit of fast drying paint on her. In this way you can tell if the hive has the same queen.

Caution

During the hot sultry part of the year, when no honey is coming in and bees are inclined to rob, bees are more difficult to requeen. This difficulty can be overcome by tacking a piece of queen excluder zinc over the candy end of the cage. The perforation is wide enough to let in the workers but too narrow to release the queen. Feeding such a colony and releasing any attendant workers that come with the queen will also help. After better weather comes, or a strong honey flow begins, release the queen by pulling up the screen.

•Balling the Queen

When a strange queen is placed in colony, the bees usually resent her presence, and consider her an intruder. This is caused by her strange new odor and her unusual actions due to her distress. Sometimes, before she has been in the hive more than a few seconds, the bees form an angry mass, clinging closely to her body (or to the queen cage she was introduced in) and smother her and tear her apart.

If the bees attempt to **ball** a queen in this way, she should be quickly rescued by puffing a little smoke at the mass, or by dropping the ball of bees into water. Introduce her by the cage method described previously.

Sometimes bees disturbed unnecessarily by the beekeeper, vandals, skunks, or another source, ball their own queen. In this case, your colony will be suddenly queenless for no apparent reason. They should start making queen cells and raise a new one. You may want to requeen such a colony with another kind of queen.

Swarms

Summer should be the most pleasant part of the beekeeping season. If colonies are brought up to strength by good spring management, about the only thing that stands between you and a honey crop is the problem of swarming. Not all colonies swarm but why some do and others do not may be genetically linked. There seems to be no one single cause for swarming, but rather a combination of factors. However, the loss of a swarm reduces the honey-making potential of a colony, particularly if

Bees that are clustering outside the hive like this need more room inside. You can either add another super or split this colony. If you do nothing, this hive may swarm. K. E. Farner Photo.

Swarm cells are found on the lower part of the frame. Such a colony should be split, taking the frames of swarm cells and placing them into a nuc. This will prevent the parent colony from swarming. A. Mullin Photo.

the colony swarms more than once.

The swarming season may be expected shortly after the time the bees are rearing the greatest amount of brood. In the northern part of the United States this is May and June; in the Gulf states, in March or April. Swarming is the bees' natural method of colony reproduction. A brood nest crowded with bees is a condition which usually leads to swarming. Attempting to relieve this condition by adding supers or providing additional ventilation will sometimes prevent swarming.

Indications of Swarming

As the swarming season comes on, you should watch for signs of swarming behavior. Bees clustering on the outside of the hive is one general sign. If a colony has been busy at work and then quits without evident reason while the other colonies are busy, and bees are clustered outside, swarming is probably near at hand. A sure sign is the presence of queen cells, called "swarm" cells. If small or initial queen cells containing eggs or larvae are found, the bees are probably contemplating swarming. These cells are usually found on the bottom of frames, hanging below the level of the frame.

Swarm Control

There are some manipulations that can reduce the chances of the colony swarming and, therefore, preserve its' productive capacity for the season.

One method of swarm control, commonly known as the Demaree method, separates the queen from the brood, relieving congestion in the brood nest. When a double story colony shows signs of swarming, all the sealed brood is placed into the upper hive body. The queen is confined to the lower super under a queen excluder,

with the unsealed brood and empty combs. The Demaree method of swarm control, or its variations, have the advantages of combining three basic swarm control measures:

1. removal of the queen
2. removal of the brood
3. separation of the queen and brood

Most of the objections to the Demaree method are that it requires finding the queen, and that the bees in the brood super above the queen excluder may build queen cells if any young larvae are present. All queen cells should be destroyed at five to eight days after making the original manipulation. Another problem is that removing brood or replacing a few frames of brood in the center of the brood nest with empty combs, may upset the delicate balance which the bees maintain. This can result in chilled brood.

Swarm controls are intensive methods which are necessary for the profitable operation of an apiary. They require skills and judgment that come only with experience. Talk to other beekeepers about how they control the swarming instinct.

On the other hand, swarms can be a convenient way to replace colonies that are winter killed or otherwise lost throughout the year. Captured swarms utilize spare equipment that would otherwise remain idle.

Hiving a Swarm with a Clipped Queen

Some beekeepers clip the wings of queens for identification and age. When the wings of all the queens in the bee yard are clipped, the problem of hiving the swarm is comparatively simple. A swarm with a clipped queen can usually be found on the ground near the hive. Sometimes they miss her entirely, and after they have been flying around in the air will go back to

Sometimes a clipped queen will swarm out, but because she can't fly, the swarm will cluster on or near the ground next to the hive. Move the parent hive, replace with an empty one and let the bees march in.

the hive where they started. By looking carefully in the grass in front of the hive, the queen can be found and put into a cage.

If the queenless swarm clusters, here is how to prevent them from swarming again. Move the original hive away, and replace it with a new box, containing frames of foundation and a frame of unsealed brood from the old colony, (this should be put in the center and the frames of foundation on the outside.)

The supers are then transferred from the parent colony to the new hive, and the cage containing the queen is thrust into the entrance. The queenless swarm will soon return to this hive. After all the bees are in, release the queen. The parent hive should be set far enough to one side so that the returning bees will not find it, but will go into the new hive.

This so depletes the parent colony that it is not able to send out an **after-swarm**. A new queen will soon start laying and you have two new hives. If you do not want to increase the number of hives in your apiary, join them back together in the fall.

A large swarm, such as this, will require at least 2 deep supers to hive.

Hiving a Swarm With an Unclipped Queen

Suppose the swarm has issued from a colony whose queen's wings are not clipped, and she accompanies the swarm in its flight and clustering. This presents quite a different problem; the bees will not return to the hive of their own will, for their queen is with them. They will probably cluster on some nearby bush or limb. Soon they fly off to a new home which "scout bees" have previously located, and so are lost to the beekeeper.

If the bees have clustered low on the branch of some tree or bush, their capture is easy. Either shake the bees into a box or basket or cut off the branch and carry it to an already prepared hive. Then shake the bees at the entrance of the hive. Some prefer spreading a sheet or newspaper in front of the hive on which to shake the bees; but, while this is a little neater, it is not essential.

Hiving such a swarm is like installing a package. Have your hive body, foundation or drawn frames ready.

When the swarm has been shaken in front of the entrance, the bees will quickly begin crawling into the hive (or can be directed into it by brushing or gently smoking). Once in, they remain there if the queen is with them. But if the bees begin running out of the hive and acting agitated, the queen has probably not entered with them. Search for her, perhaps under the hive, attended by a little group of bees, or at the original clustering place. Cage her and place her in the new hive.

If the bees chance to cluster in a place where they cannot be shaken down, as on a large branch or at the crotch of a tree or on a fence post, brush them off into the box or basket with a bee brush. Close the box (an old cardboard one is good), or cover it with an old sheet or pillowcase. Unless the container is ventilated, the captured bees should be carried to the hive and released as soon as possible.

Once the bees start to march into the hive, watch to see if you can spot the queen. She might still be in the cluster above. This large swarm will draw out beautiful foundation. C. Watts Photo.

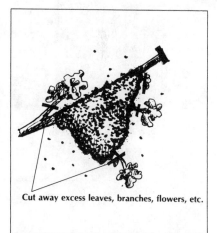

Cut away excess leaves, branches, flowers, etc.

A smaller swarm can be carried to their new home and shaken in front. Look for the queen as the bees will not stay there if she is missing. D. Sammataro Photo.

•Capturing Swarms

A swarm will sometimes cluster on a limb beyond your reach. If it cannot be reached with an ordinary step ladder, perhaps the best advice is to leave them. A swarm of bees is not worth broken bones.

A beekeeper is often called on to remove bees that have become established in the walls of a building. Unless the bees are in a place where the siding can be easily removed to expose the brood nest, or the entry hole is near the ground so that the bees can be trapped out, such requests are best referred to the professional exterminator. Trapping bees from a building or tree is not impossible but it does require patience, ingenuity and considerable time.

However, we strongly suggest that every effort be made to capture swarms. If you are unable to personally retrieve it, know who to contact who can. There are several machines, nets, etc. that can aid in swarm capture. Also, this added effort will help better public relations.

Multiple Swarms

Another emergency that may confront the beginner is when two or more swarms without clipped queens issue simultaneously. If small (basket ball sized or smaller), combine them into the same hive.

If you spot a marked queen that you wish to keep, cage her. If not, let the queens sort themselves out.

Swarm Prevention

Preventing a colony from swarming is very important if you want to produce a crop of honey. Studies have shown that normally 66% of the bees leave with the swarm. The remaining 34% have to carry on brood rearing and housekeeping activities as before. This leaves very few to gather nectar.

It is much more difficult to prevent swarming some seasons than others. A heavy honey flow, following a light one will usually stop all efforts to swarm. If the flow continues light all the season, bees will often continue to swarm until the intake of nectar slows down.

Again, when seasons are favorable for heavy brood rearing, watch for these signals:
1. If too much heat causes the bees to cluster out, then the obvious remedy is to see that the hive is properly shaded and that the entrance is opened up all the way. In extremely hot sultry weather or in some semi-tropical localities, it may be necessary to raise the hive off the ground on a tall hive stand to allow better air flow.
2. If the brood nest is congested, that is, if the hive has a large force

A colony this congested will soon swarm, especially if swarm cells are present. If not, give them some honey supers above a queen excluder for the bees to work on. C. Pinkham Photo.

of bees, young and old, and if there is a large amount of emerging brood, more room must be provided.

The queen should be put with the young brood below and kept there with a queen excluder. The sealed brood should be put above. A colony can also be divided into two at this time. The sealed brood in the top will shortly emerge, giving room for honey storage.

3. Colonies headed by young queens are much less inclined to swarm than those with queens a year or more old.

4. Giving a super of drawn combs is much more effective in preventing swarming than giving a super of sheets of comb foundation. It is for this reason bees are more inclined to swarm in the production of comb honey than extracted honey.

5. After the bees start work in the supers, either for comb or extracted honey, and the flow continues, there is less likelihood of the bees swarming. So it is important to get the bees started on the supers.

Artificial Swarming

This is done by shaking most of the bees, together with the queen, from the combs either into their own hive or into a new hive placed where the old one stood. As a rule, it is best to find and cage the queen before shaking any combs. At least two of the combs should be put back into the parent hive without shaking so there are enough bees to take care of the brood. The parent hive is then set to one side.

Pick a comb containing the largest queen-cells; it should not be shaken, for shaking the combs may injure the young queens. Destroy all other queen cells.

Artificial swarms are used for comb honey production, to prevent swarming bees from flying off, or to make another hive (called an **increase**).

Dividing Colonies

If you wish to make two colonies from one strong one, without shaking all the bees, here's what you do. If a colony has a vigorous queen and has built up a strong population before the honey flow, you can divide it. In this manner a colony that was purchased from another beekeeper or an overwintered one can be the source of a new colony.

The colony that is to be divided must be reasonably strong, in two or

---

Pick a frame containing the largest queen cells and place it into a nuc. Queen cells are fragile and easily damaged (like the center cell at the bottom), so handle with care. J. A. Schmidt Photo.

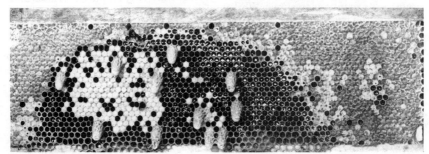

more brood chambers, with enough bees to cover most of the frames, have ample honey and at least 7 - 10 frames of brood in all stages of development. The division should be made in late spring, early enough to allow the new queen to mate and put on enough honey for the winter. Most early divisions are made in advance of the first minor flow. This gives the new colony several weeks to develop and the parent colony time to replace the brood and bees before the main flow.

Order queens for the planned division well in advance so they will arrive at the proper time. Sometimes queen cells can be used in place of a mated queen for the division, but they may not always be available. A mated queen introduced to the new colony is much more satisfactory.

Equipment required for the division should be prepared beforehand. You will need one deep hive body filled with ten frames of drawn comb or foundation plus a specially prepared inner cover. This inner cover should have the center opening screened on both sides, creating a double screen barrier to prevent the two queens from coming into contact. A fine mesh window screen is best. If the inner cover does not have the half round ventilating port in the rim, cut out a section of the rim about 1" in length to serve as an exit for the bees.

Begin by taking two frames of sealed brood and a frame of unsealed brood, along with the accompanying bees, from the parent colony. Put them in the empty deep super. While removing the brood frames, examine each one carefully to be certain that the queen is not there. It may be to your advantage to locate the queen in advance and put aside the frame she is on until the division is completed. Place the frame of unsealed brood between the combs of sealed brood so they will be over the screened hole of the inner cover beneath.

Place your new caged queen on one side of the comb of unsealed brood, after unplugging the candy side. Before covering, you may wish to shake more bees from the parent colony into the new unit. To this new hive, add at least two frames containing honey and pollen, placing one on each side of the brood. Fill the remaining space with drawn comb or foundation.

Two or three frames of sealed brood plus bees will provide enough workers to feed a newly introduced queen, or keep a queen cell warm.

In the parent hive, shove all the remaining combs together in the center of the brood body, making sure that the queen is still on the comb which has been set aside. Fill any empty spaces with empty drawn or foundation frames placed on either side of the brood frames.

After the parent colony has received its full complement of frames, place the newly prepared division and the special inner cover on top of the parent colony with the exit hole facing the opposite direction of the parent colony's entrance. The inner and outer cover which had been on the parent colony is now placed over all.

You now have a potentially vigorous colony and a division which should build up rapidly if conditions are favorable. The parent colony will soon recoup the brood and bees used for the division. Heat passing up through the screened inner cover hole from the bottom colony will help the new colony maintain brood rearing temperature while the double screen will prevent the two queens from coming into contact. Even though some of the field bees may fly out of the new colony and return to the parent hive, they will soon be replaced by the emerging young bees. Facing the exit hole of the upper unit in the opposite direction from the parent colony may cut down this loss.

Check the progress of the top unit in one week, noting particularly if the queen has been released and is laying eggs. If no evidence of eggs or larvae is seen during this inspection and the queen is not in the cage and cannot be found on the combs, either order a replacement queen or rejoin hive. There is always the possibility that a fledgling colony will not accept the first queen or that the queen fails to survive the introductory period for some reason.

If honey stores given at the time

Once the division is strong enough, it can be set off on it's own stand. Keep feeding it until it will eat no more. Notice the nuc on top of the hive. It probably contains a queen cell. S.L.P.D. Photo.

75

of the division appear to be insufficient, feed the new division until it has organized a field force and is bringing in nectar. Watch for food shortages if the weather is unsuitable for flying and foraging. Use an internal type feeder to feed sugar syrup or give additional combs of honey, as this method will minimize the threat of robbing.

In a month to six weeks when the division is well established, set it off on its own bottom board.

These manipulations are apt to be more successful during the time that a nectar flow is in progress. If the nectar flow should cease, it is important to have a reserve of food in the division.

Robbing

Robbing occurs when bees steal honey or other food not gathered by themselves. It is much easier to prevent robbing than to stop it once

---

A beekeeper may inadvertently start a robbing frenzy by leaving combs and supers exposed for too long a time during a nectar dearth. USDA Forsythe Photo.

started. It can be serious if a prolonged **dearth** (or nectarless) period ensues.

Any beekeeper may inadvertently bring on a robbing frenzy, during hive manipulation or honey harvest. The bees themselves will often start robbing by attacking a weak colony to secure its too feebly guarded stores, especially early in the season. A strong colony keeps a sufficient guard of defenders at the entrance. Further, if the weak colony is diseased, robbing can spread the infection throughout your apiary.

Once bees get a taste of honey or other sweets which they have not gathered, they become greatly excited. The longer the robbing continues, the wilder the robber bees become until the weak colony is destroyed. It is true that robbing often starts from slight causes, but it does not take long for an uproar to develop. Bees coming home loaded with fully-ripened honey or other sweets, excite the other bees of the hive, which then rush to get some of the same. It is this sort of fracas that should cure any beginner of being so careless as to allow robbing to get started again.

Factors Leading to Robbing

When there is no incoming nectar you can expect robbing to start. If you are harvesting honey during this time, use an escape board with bee escapes rather than brushing or blowing off bees. But if the cover does not fit bee-tight, robbing will start. Be careful in adjusting the bee-escape below the supers to see that the cover above is not warped.

Supers above an escape board are unprotected, and are therefore tempting targets for robbers. Remember: A worker bee can squeeze through a hole as small as .163 inch, so cover all cracks with tape if you have problems.

Robbing can also be started if sugar syrup is carelessly spilled on the ground, honey frames or supers are left uncovered, or wet extracted supers are given to bees.

•Robbing During Extraction

When extracting during a honey dearth, it is important that all windows in the extracting room are screened. The door of the room should be solid, not screened, otherwise there will always be bees flying around, and some will get in every time it is opened.

After you have finished, you may feed back wet supers and cappings to individual colonies. Do this late in the afternoon to deter robbers. Place the cappings in a screened bag and place it in an empty super above a colony. Cover it tightly. The bees will soon clean up all leftover honey.

•Robbing Weak Colonies

Weak colonies are vulnerable to robbing, especially if they are well provided with honey and if their entrances are large. This is particularly true in the spring when colonies are weak from winter losses. To prevent robbing, reduce entrances to 1-2".

You can save a weak colony from being robbed out by moving it or throwing handfulls of grass at the entrance to impede the flight of robbers. R. L. Parker Photo.

Also, moving a weak hive to another yard, joining it with a larger colony, or moving the robbing hive will help the situation.

If robbing has just started, it can usually be controlled by reducing the entrance, and throwing a bunch of damp hay or grass over the front of the hive that is being robbed (see illus.). Robber bees do not like to dodge through such obstructions, for they cannot make their "quick get away." If the entrance is reduced in this way on a hot day, extra shade should be provided for the hive.

Where there is a general uproar in the apiary caused by robbing, reduce entrances of all weak colonies; see there is no possible opening to honey anywhere, then leave, and let the bees alone.

Robbing or Playflights?

Beginners often mistake young bees at play for robbers. Sometimes a large number will be seen flying busily around the front of the hive, usually in the afternoon. There is a sense of great activity there, while other colonies are quiet. Closer investigation, however, shows the young bees testing their wings. Under such circumstances there is total absence of any fighting. There is no sneaking in the entrance nor darting around, nor is there the high, alarming note of excited bees peculiar to a robbing foray. In a playflight, the unusual flying will soon subside. If it is a case of robbing, the excitement will increase with unremitting fury.

•Getting Bees from a Bee Tree

Occasionally you can get a colony of bees from a bee tree from a nearby woods. It should be stated that this is an expensive and in some cases, dangerous way to get them. However, it can be educational and interesting.

Sometimes you, as a beekeeper, get a call from a frantic landowner or tree company who found a tree full of bees. Here is how you go about getting them out of the tree and into a hive.

First, call an experienced bee-keeper to help — it will be easier with two people. Cut down the tree, if it is not already down. When it falls, bee veils and a smoker will be needed. The continual chopping at the cavity where the bees are, after the tree has fallen, will have a tendency to quiet them. The bees are so disorganized that they will scarcely sting.

To get inside the brood nest, it will be necessary to split the log in half. By having a caged queen handy, the bees will be easier to collect. Only good combs containing worker brood should be transferred into the frames. Cut the combs carefully to fit empty frames. Using rubber bands or string, secure them to the wooden frame. Put

To get bees from a house or tree, set a weak queenright colony on a stand as near the entrance as possible. Construct a cone of window screen and point it at the hive's entrance. Bees from the house, unable to return there, go into the new hive box. D. Sammataro Photo.

these frames into a hive body to which you have already stapled on the bottom board. Put all combs of honey into a covered bucket, the ruined frames of brood in another.

Now you have to get the rest of the bees into the hive box. Wait until evening when the bees stop flying. Brush bees into a bucket, use a special bee vacuum, or place the hive with the frames of banded combs and queen cage in such a way that the bees can crawl in. Sometimes you can hang the queen cage in a nearby branch and by inducing the bees to swarm out, (with smoking), they will cluster on her.

Once the bees are all inside, block the entrance of the hive with a screen, and tack down the inner cover. The hive must be bee-tight before attempting to move it. All parts should be securely fastened together. Place the whole hive in a truck and move to a permanent location. Usually a bee tree will not have much honey and a comparatively small number of bees.

•Getting Bees from a House or Tree

By using a **wire cone escape**, a device which allows bees to pass out of an enclosure, but not return, you can get bees out of a house or bee tree. If the bees are not too high up, or located in the sides of a building and it is not practical to remove the siding, the cone escape can be used.

The opening to the nest should be covered with the cone escape, so the bees can come out but cannot return. Place in front of this escape a hive box or nuc, set on a temporary shelf. There should be a frame of brood and a queen cell or queen from some other colony in the hive. Fill remaining space with frames of foundation.

The bees coming out of the bee tree or building will not be able to return because of the cone escape. They will then enter the hive. All other openings to the original colony must be closed. In the course of three weeks all the bees except the queen and some young brood will have gone into the modern hive. Spray the remaining bees with an insecticide and plug up hole.

Laying Workers

Ordinarily, worker bees are imperfectly developed females. Under certain circumstances, however, their organs become developed to such an extent that they are able to lay eggs. They are then called laying workers. Such eggs, however, always develop into drones, since fertilization of workers is impossible; only fertilized eggs can produce females. The eggs are scattered here and there, sometimes two or three eggs to a cell.

Such a condition can be caused when a virgin queen is lost in mating and there are no young larvae left to raise another queen. After two or three weeks, the colony may choose certain workers to be "queens" by feeding them royal jelly to stimulate their ovaries. To get rid of them, strenuous measures must be adopted, since it is very difficult to distinguish them from ordinary workers.

For the beginner having a few colonies, it is best to distribute the bees to other normal colonies. Another method is to place a new queenright hive on the stand of a laying worker colony. Remove the old hive about 10 feet away and shake all the bees onto the ground. Those able to fly will return to this new, queenright hive, presumably leaving the laying workers behind.

Drone Layers

Finding a colony with mostly drone brood, and with eggs placed irregularly, does not necessarily prove the presence of laying workers. Improperly fertilized or non-mated queens will lay only **drone eggs**.

A drone layer may also be a failing queen due to disease or old age. She should be found and killed, then give the colony frames of brood in different stages of development; or introduce a new queen.

Sudden Queen Loss

When a colony suddenly loses a queen, it has eggs and young larvae from which to rear a new one. But sometimes a colony fails to raise a new queen. If there are no eggs present, or little brood, give it a frame or two of capped and uncapped larvae. Sometimes you can also give it a frame containing queen cells, eggs, young larvae and emerging brood. If this condition arises only five or six weeks before the honey flow, the colony will not be able to build up in time to take advantage of the flow. It will not have a laying queen for 20 or 25 days. If this is the case, unite the colony with another queenright colony.

Drifting

This phenomena, where field bees lose track of which hive is home and go into another, is called drifting. It is most common if you have 10 or more hives in a row. Soon you will notice that the colonies at the ends are stronger than those in the middle.

To prevent this, put groups of hives together in a semi-circular or horseshoe pattern, put up a wind break or other vertical marker, or stagger short rows of hives. Another way to reduce drifting, if you must have long rows, is to alternate the entrances front, back, front, etc., down the row.

9. Late Season Management

Equalizing Colonies

You have now made it through the main honey flow. Hopefully you took off some honey, and were able to taste the natural sweetness produced by your own bees. But now cool weather is setting in, and the days are getting shorter. There are several things to look for now, especially if your colony is still weak. So suit up and do a quick look inside your hive.

By fall it is important to have all colonies as nearly even in strength as is possible. There are several ways of doing this:
1. Unite weak colonies into one.
2. Take sealed brood from the strong and give to the weak.
3. Buy package bees to boost weak colonies.

Any of these three ways should bring the colonies up to about the same numerical strength. In the fall, a weak colony in the northern states will not withstand the rigors of winter. A colony not up to par is a liability rather than an asset. A main axiom of beekeeping is to *count your losses in the fall,* not in the spring.

The Newspaper Method

Since you cannot just add two colonies together without the members fighting, a good way is to unite by the newspaper method.

The stronger colony should be on the bottom. Remove covers and spread a single sheet of newspaper on the top bars. The weaker colony to be moved should be set on top of this newspaper in early morning, before

Late season swarms or weak colonies should be united to a strong one by using a sheet of newspaper as a temporary barrier.
I. Sibert Photo.

they have started flying. If the weather is cool, there will be no danger of the upper hive suffocating. But if the weather is hot, prick a few holes with your hive tool through the paper. The bees will unite so slowly that there will be no fighting between the two colonies. Feeding one or both colonies also insures quick acceptance. You can remove the inferior queen (taken from either colony), or you can leave both queens. They will determine which is strongest and which will survive.

Taking Brood from Strong Colonies

Brood should only be taken from a colony that has reached peak population.

Select one or more of your strongest colonies. Count the number of frames containing capped brood. If there are more than 10, you may transfer a frame or two of capped brood to a weak colony. Make sure the weaker colony has enough worker bees to cover these new frames to keep the brood warm. If it does not, unite the colony with a stronger one.

Both colonies involved should be free of disease. If there is the slightest suspicion that disease is present, do not transfer brood.

Using A Booster Package

Of the three methods, the package method quickly saves the colony and provides the hive with instant bees. By uniting, you lose one colony, and by taking brood you could spread disease. Packages of young bees present fewest difficulties. The bees are young, and therefore will survive the winter. If your weak colony has only a handful of bees and a young queen, give them three pounds of bees without a queen. If the weak hive has an old queen, either you can kill her and requeen or you can unite this colony.

To add a queenless package to a weak colony, gorge the package with syrup, until it will take no more. Then dump the bees at the hive entrance, just as you did when installing your spring package. Feed the weak colony sugar syrup a few days before, during, and after this. Bees that are filled with syrup are not inclined to fight.

Fall is Requeening Time

Requeening may be necessary at this time of the year, especially if you have a failing or missing queen. Since it is too late in the year for bees to raise a new one, you must provide them with a mated queen.

Queens are cheapest in the early fall months. If the old or failing queens are replaced by young vigorous queens at this time, the hive will soon be filled with brood, which means young bees will go into winter. Colonies often die during winter because they have old queens which fail to start laying in the early spring.

Select a queen breeder of known reputation. Remember, some queens will fall below the standard advertised, or will be superseded early. For specific methods on requeening, see Chapter 8.

Fall Feeding

Natural Stores vs. Sugar Syrup

Well ripened sealed honey is preferred to sugar or artificial stores for overwintered colonies. Even during mid-winter, well-ripened, disease free honey is superior to sugar syrup. Frames of honey will also contain some stored pollen (bee bread) which is vital for brood rearing.

Straight sugar syrup lacks the necessary food elements that bees need. However, there are times when sugar syrup is better to feed than honey. In late fall, while the weather is relatively warm, a thick syrup of 2-1/2 parts sugar to 1 part hot water is best. Medication for foulbrood and nosema diseases can also be added. The bees will quickly consume this, going into the winter with medicated syrup in their stomachs. That way they can save their honey stores, with preserved pollen, for spring brood rearing when it is most needed.

•Feeding Syrup

Friction top five- and ten- pound plastic pails, or gallon glass jars, make convenient feeders. The top is perforated with nail holes, then filled with sugar syrup and inverted over the inner cover hole, or over the top bars. An empty super is put over the pail, and the outer cover, with a weight, is placed over all.

There are other kinds of feeders you can use as well. Talk to some beekeepers to see what they use and try them out.

Making Syrup

Use granulated, white sugar only, as brown sugar or molasses contains many impurities. Slowly add the sugar to **hot** water and stir until it's all dissolved. Remember, the proportions of the syrup for fall or winter feeding is 2 to 2-1/2 sugar to 1 of hot water.

High Fructose Corn Syrup

This is a syrup made from corn starch and is used by many beekeepers. The commonly fed formula is 52% glucose, 42% fructose and water. Check prices in your area, as in some regions it is cost prohibitive. Also, it is usually delivered only by tank car loads, so storage problems should be investigated before purchasing.

Feeding Dry Sugar

Sometimes feeding sugar syrup involves more work than you can give, and it may cause robbing if syrup is spilled (see Chapter 8; Robbing).

Dry granulated sugar placed on top of a sheet of newspaper gives bees emergency rations late winter or early spring. R. A. Stauble Photo.

Dry granulated sugar can be scattered around the hole on top of the inner cover. At first the bees will hesitate and not take it, but as long as they can bring in water, they can dissolve the sugar crystals. If the colony is large, give three or four pounds of dry sugar, for it is astonishing how rapidly bees will eat it up.

Candy

Some beekeepers make a fondant candy, which is a soft, sugar product easy to manipulate. There are various fondant candy recipes in most cookbooks.

A faster 'mock' candy is made by mixing clean disease-free honey with powdered sugar into a dough. Place on top bars or around inner cover hole.

Fall Management

There are at least three requirements that each colony must meet during the fall months: good queens, plenty of pollen and ample honey.

Many beekeepers practice requeening in the early fall. As already mentioned, young queens introduced at this time will produce populous colonies of young bees to go into winter.

Beekeepers should see to it that each colony is well supplied with stores in the fall; this means both honey and pollen. Pollen is stored as "bee bread" under a cap of honey in the frames. If there is little honey in a hive, give frames or supers of honey. Or, feed heavily and early enough for bees to convert and store the syrup and put it in the frames.

By the time the first snow falls, a normal two deep colony should have the lower story full of bees/brood, the upper full of honey.

Wintering

In The Southern States

The biggest problem with wintering in the South is the danger of starvation. The bees can fly every few days, gather a little pollen, and sometimes a little nectar. This stimulates brood rearing, which results in a large quantity of stores being consumed. Unless ample honey and pollen have been left on, the bees are liable to starve to death. Where the bees are running short of stores they should be given light 1:1 (water and sugar) syrup, or a shallow or half-depth super of honey.

Experience in southern California, Arizona, Texas, Georgia, and Alabama shows that a super of honey and pollen is not only a good guarantee against starvation, but against a failure next spring and summer.

In parts of Florida and Louisiana, this reserve may not be needed. The beginner should know, however, that in some years there will be a sufficient nectar supply, while in other years, there will be no nectar, and the bees will die unless fed.

No winter packing around the hives will be needed in any of the southern states where winter temperatures range from 45-68°F (10-20°C). In fact, the bees are better off without it. It is advantageous, however, to have the hives screened from prevailing winds. Brood rearing will have a severe setback unless the hives are protected by a windbreak of underbrush, trees, fences, or buildings.

In The Northern States (and High Altitudes)

Wintering in the North is quite different than in the South. In the colder climates, it is not so much a question of starvation, as one of extreme cold, causing bees to consume stores. If there is insufficient honey, starvation can occur.

Bees in cold climates form a cluster called a **winter cluster**. This means when the air temperatures drop below 57°F (13.9°C), the bees form a ball inside the hive. This ball of bees generates metabolic heat, and moves about eating honey. When the queen resumes laying in mid-winter, the cluster temperature increases to 93°F so the eggs will hatch.

It is important to have a large reserve of natural stores in the food chamber or brood rearing will be curtailed. If insufficient, the bees will stop brood rearing at a time when it should be at its peak. It is common practice to winter in a two-story hive with a large cluster of bees. To attempt to winter a small colony in a single-story hive is taking a chance. In regions where winter temperatures are 20°F (-6.7°C) or below, give each colony at least 85-100 pounds of honey.

•Windbreaks

Next in importance is an adequate windbreak, consisting of a heavy growth of bushes, young trees

An apiary should be protected from prevailing winter winds (NW). A slatted snow fence or other fencing can be used. The trees provide summer shade. T. Doonan Photo.

or a specially constructed fence. The boards should be spaced far enough apart to let the wind filter slowly through. This spacing of the boards breaks the force of the wind. If it was a solid fence, the wind will glance up and then, impelled by the upper current of the air, dive downward hitting the hives as if there was no windbreak at all.

Wind chill is an important factor on clusters. Experience shows that where hives are out in the open and exposed to cold wind, bees will often die; those protected by windbreaks more often survive.

• Winter Packing

Hives subjected to extended peri-ods of sub-freezing weather should be wrapped or packed in such a way to provide insulation and wind protection. There are various methods and materials for this, and only by talking with experienced beekeepers and inspectors in your area can you make an intelligent decision.

Some beekeepers merely wrap each hive with tar paper or cover it with a special cover. As long as an upper and lower entrance is provided, that is all there is to it.

Others cluster two or four hives together as a unit, stuff the spaces between with straw, fiberglass or other material, then cover it with tar paper. As long as internal hive air filled with moisture can escape, the

Some beekeepers wrap their hives with tar paper. Provide top and bottom entrances so bees can fly out in good weather.

bees should do fine. When this moisture cannot escape, the packing material will become water logged from excess moisture and freeze solid, and will do more harm than good.

When Packing is Required

It is recommended to pack colonies when the temperature is around 0°F (-17.8°C) for long periods of time. If the winters are extremely cold and continue close to zero through to spring, it may be advisable to winter bees in a **bee cellar** instead. See how other beekeepers winter their hives in your area.

If the climate is dry, packing may be omitted as long as the bees are out of the wind.

Colonies wrapped in fall should be large enough to fill a two-story hive, have a young queen, and be placed in front of a good windbreak.

• Top Entrances

A top entrance can be as simple as

an auger hole 5/8" to 1" in diameter, bored below the hand hold of the top hive body. The purpose of this upper entrance is to allow moisture to escape at or near the top. Without such openings the bees may become wet, freeze, chill and die. These holes can later be corked. There are even screened ventilated tops especially designed for winter/summer use.

An upper entrance can be made by drilling a 1" auger hole under the hand hold. Place inner cover so the rim is down, and then a weighted outer cover. Reduce the entrance and the colony is ready for winter.

To provide an upper entrance or flight hole in a wrapped hive, press the paper close up to the hole, cut a small opening in the paper and tack it carefully to the hive around the upper entrance.

We believe the upper entrance or flight hole has at least two advantages:
1. It permits bees that need to fly during the winter to get out of the hive, instead of having to use the restricted winter entrance at the bottom.
2. The upper flight hole helps to expel some of the excess moisture

that may accumulate during cold weather.

When there is a bottom entrance only, it may become clogged with dead bees, ice, or snow.

Bees need to be able to fly outside on warm days. Since they store their feces, they must be able to fly out and defecate, otherwise, they would foul the inside of the hive.

Unpacking in the Spring

The packing should not be removed until settled warm spring weather comes. This time will vary according to the latitude. Wait for the temperatures to even out before unpacking.

Unpacking too early may cause brood to be chilled if weather snaps back to cold.

•Wintering Problems

Dysentery

During late winter or early spring in the northern states, the fronts and sides of the hives can be spotted with dark yellow or brown

A lightly spotted hive in the spring is usually alright, but could be from fermented honey or nosema disease. Such hives may need extra help in the spring. R. A. Morse Photo.

spots. This indicates that the colony may not have wintered well and that the bees are suffering from **dysentery**.

Dysentery is usually caused by bad honey stores and long confinement during an especially hard, long winter. Bees normally fly out of the colony to defecate. If they are forced to stay inside the hive, they will soil the interior.

Bees winter best on well ripened honey that is not high in indigestible material, such as **honeydew**. The condition may also be made worse by inadequate upper ventilation, resulting in condensation of water inside the hive.

When the cluster is too small to maintain body heat, or when there is insufficient wind protection, bees are required to eat and exercise to raise the temperature in the cluster. This causes the intestinal tract to become clogged and the bees get a case of diarrhea. The only real remedy for this situation is warm sunshine, during which the bees can fly and discharge their feces. Where the colonies are strong, this flight, if followed by another in a week or ten days, will save the colony. If the hive is badly spotted with dark brown spots in January or February (in the north), it may be considered doomed.

Another cause of spotting may be **Nosema disease**. See Chapter 11; Diseases and Pests of Honey Bees.

As you can't control the weather, the obvious remedy is to see that the colonies are strong in the fall, have good stores, occupy two stories and are well protected according to your locality.

However, a little spotting on the hives as a result of a good day of sunshine, when the bees can fly, indicates nothing out of the ordinary. Healthy bees will always spot some after flight in early spring. This is perfectly normal. It is only a badly spotted hive with dark, ill smelling spots where the colony is doomed. As soon as it succumbs, its entrance should be closed to prevent robbing.

Don't Disturb Bees During Winter

Bees in winter quarters should not be disturbed. The temptation to open hives during midwinter to see how they are doing should be restrained. Don't do it unless you think the hive is starving. To disturb bees often during midwinter is a good way to kill them.

You can tell if your hive is in trouble if you have it on a scale. A hive showing rapid or steady weight loss, and no gain, may require attention.

• Early Spring

By January or February, the queen will again lay eggs and brood rearing commences. This means the eggs and larvae are incubated at 93°F (33.9°C), even though the outside temperature may be below freezing.

(So you see the need for good stores and wind protection). By the time spring is here to stay, each colony should have at least 4 or 5 frames of capped brood. It usually takes a colony about eight weeks to build up to full strength, ready for the honey flow.

Weak colonies in the spring should be treated the same as weak ones in the fall — unite, add brood or add queenless packages.

Spring Feeding

Bees usually do not starve in the winter. When brood rearing is in full swing, and most of the stored honey is consumed, the bees are very vulnerable. If a spring flow of crocus, willow or fruit fails to materialize (due to cold or wet weather) such populous colonies could die of starvation almost overnight. Carefully monitor such colonies and be prepared for emergency feeding. Dry sugar, honey frames, pollen substitutes and sugar syrup should all be ready on a moment's notice.

Two hives can be packed and wrapped together. This old orchard is sheltered and as long as no sprays are used, is a good location for bees. J. Staby Photo.

10. Packaging & Marketing Hive Products

Extracted Honey

One of the most satisfying accomplishments in beekeeping is turning out a clear sparkling bottle of delicious honey. A superior jar of honey begins in the bee yard. Only well ripened and well flavored honey should be extracted. Honeys with flavors that are judged not acceptable for table use are best left for the bees as winter stores or sold as bakery grade.

An attractive way of packaging one pound jars of honey.

Color may not necessarily be an indicator of quality, since many of the darker honeys have excellent flavor. Even those with a unique flavor may have a special appeal for some people, if they are attractively packed and properly labeled by source. These include buckwheat, palmetto, orange, and sunflower honey.

A 5 gallon plastic pail fitted with a honey gate is an excellent way for hobbyists to settle and bottle honey.

A previous discussion in Chapter 7 told you about straining and settling honey. Allow honey to settle for at least 24 hours for the wax particles and air bubbles to rise to the top. This leaves a reasonably clear honey. It can then be drawn off into pails or bottled. A **honey gate** fitted to a 60 pound pail is another way to fill the glass bottles.

If the honey is to be sold direct to the customer for immediate use, it may not be necessary to heat it. If it is to be stored for a while, though, it is best to take it out of the holding tank and store it in 60 pound pails. Bottle only enough honey that can be sold quickly. Store the rest of your crop in pails or drums, in *cool* shady places, not exposed to direct sunlight or excessive heat. Too often, stored honey is ruined by improper storage.

Storing Honey

Honey is a good keeper, and properly stored will last for years. But how do you "properly store" it?

•Changes In Stored Honey

Honey will darken with age and after awhile, the volatile oils that give a particular honey its flavor will dissipate. If stored at room temperature, honey will turn black and have an unpleasant taste in about 10 years. If stored at high temperatures, this process speeds up.

While drums, pails and cans are used to hold honey, glass containers are best for long-term storage. Otherwise metal containers should be lined with a protective, food-approved liner.

The best way to store honey for a long time is to *freeze it*.

Granulation

One problem with stored honey is the fact that eventually, most honeys will **crystallize,** or **granulate.**

The granulation of honey is a physical change in liquid honey brought about by several factors. Honey is a super saturated solution, meaning there are more solids than liquids in the solution (remember, honey is only 18% water). Only glucose "turns to sugar" while fructose and sucrose remain in solution as a liquid. Some honeys granulate much faster than others, some not at all.

Granulation occurs when sugar crystals come out of liquid solution into a solid state. Many people think this is spoiled honey, but that only happens when honey ferments. In order for granulation to begin, there must be a "seed", like a piece of dust, pollen or a sugar crystal.

Honeys with a higher percentage of fructose, such as tupelo and sage, are slow to granulate, while those with a higher proportion of glucose are the quickest to granulate. Honeys from oilseed rape (*Brassica napus*) and dandelion (*Taraxacum officinale*) crystallize very quickly.

If honey does granulate, it can be heated to re-liquify it (see below).

Fermentation

Honey contains natural yeast spores that will grow if the moisture of honey is too high initially, or increases after harvest. As any wine or beer maker knows, fermenting yeasts produce carbon dioxide and alcohol. This happens either by honey absorbing moisture in the air, or when honey partially granulates, which increases the moisture content of the remaining liquid, as the glucose crystallizes out. This does not happen if the honey granulates hard, only with soft granulated honey.

Fermenting honey will foam, bubble, and taste sour or alcoholic. It is hard to save honey that has fermented.

To control fermentation, store honey below 50°F (10°C), or heat it to 145°F (63°C) for 30 minutes or 160°F (71°C) for 1 minute, then cool it rapidly.

Straining and Filtering

Commercial honey packers will filter heated honey through diatomaceous earth, under pressure, to collect all the particulate matter honey might carry. If done properly, the flavor of honey should be preserved. In this way, any seed crystals are filtered out, which extends the shelf life of honey and keeps it from granulating.

Most beekeepers use wire or nylon filters (cloth contaminates honey with lint). If heated to 120°F (49°C), honey will strain easily. If honey has floating wax particles, make sure *not to heat it more than* 148°F (64°C), or you could melt the beeswax suspended in honey; this will give the honey a waxy taste. Also, overheating can ruin the delicate flavor of your product, or actually destroy it.

Heating Honey

Honey flows faster when warm. This fact makes honey easier to extract, strain and bottle. It also speeds up the clarification of incorporated air bubbles during extracting and filtering. Bubbles will rise to the top, leaving honey below clear and clean. There are several methods used to heat honey.

Commercial beekeepers use water-jacketed bottling tanks. If you do not wish to spend too much money on equipment, you can devise innovative methods that utilize the water-jacketed tanks, but hold 20 - 40 gallons of honey. They can also be used as a settling, heating and bottling tank. This type of tank can be fitted with a honey gate, made especially for honey and syrups.

An adjustable flow gate that delivers a fairly large flow from an inch and a quarter outlet will fill larger containers quickly. A lightweight honey jar filler, with a lever control and a quick valve action, is recommended for smaller containers. The bottle filler gives precise control, particularly when honey is hot and can be delivered from a pressurized bottling tank. Packing honey hot, at least 120°F (49°C) will keep air bubbles to a minimum, and make the job faster. Cover jars as soon as possible, before honey cools, to keep out dust, thus delaying granulation. Stack hot jars to cool quickly, and then pack in boxes.

Pails can be heated in warm water baths, at 125°F (52°C) for a few days, strained and bottled. Strained, bottled honey can be heated to 145°F (63°C) to melt any sugar crystals and extend shelf life to 6 or more months. Make sure caps are on, to keep out dust or other air-borne contaminants. Stack hot bottles to cool quickly.

Re-Liquefying Honey

When honey is purchased or stored in bulk containers, such as a 60 pound pail, it will probably be granulated and must be re-liquefied. Light colored honey requires less care since it is harder to scorch than dark.

One way to do this is in a **warming cabinet**, heated to 140°F (60°C). Dry heat cabinets, holding from one to several pails, are sometimes used. This allows heated air to circulate evenly around the honey. The cabinet must be insulated to be efficient. Be aware that this form of heating honey could damage the honey if it is left there more than 24 hours. It is better if the temperature is higher (160°F - 71°C) and the liquid honey is allowed to run out continuously so it can be rapidly heated/cooled and bottled.

A more common method is a water-jacketed tank-type heater which holds two or more pails. An electric coil heating element or steam heat, brings the temperature of the water up to or slightly above that required for honey, 160-180°F (71-82°C).

Electric immersion heaters, though slower, will do a satisfactory job if the water volume is not too great. Never apply heat directly to the bottom of the honey container. Place pails so they have free space around all sides, and use strips of wood *under* the honey pails to allow hot water to circulate freely. Don't forget to loosen the top first, then bring the water level up to the top.

Use a honey thermometer to keep

a close check of the temperature of the honey. Some closed heaters have a thermostat that can accurately control the water temperature. The flavor of honey is easily lost by over heating.

Once honey is brought to the desired temperature, it should be bottled immediately. If it is necessary to strain the honey after heating and before bottling, and this is a wise precaution, the honey must be transferred to another container with an open top over which a strainer of nylon or other fine material is stretched. Allow the nylon to "bag" down into the bottling tank as far as possible; this prevents the stream of honey pouring through the strainer from incorporating a lot of air. The fewer air bubbles, the clearer the honey will be. Let the honey stand two or more hours before bottling, so air bubbles can rise to the top. Warm honey will clear faster than cool.

(Right) The square 2-1/2 pound jars are usually used for chunk comb honey. (Below) Standard queen line jars come in 8 oz., 1, 2, 3 and 5 pound sizes.

Bottling Honey

Use standard containers that show honey to it's best advantage. Bottles for packing honey are usually glass, although plastic containers are also popular, and have several advantages. Popular sizes range from the eight ounce to the five pound jar. Pint and quart fruit jars are excellent reusable containers and their use should be considered when sales are made direct to the customer. Novelty packs,

(Right) Consumers prefer these plastic containers for easy use. (Above) Gourmet shops tend to carry fancier pottery honey pots.

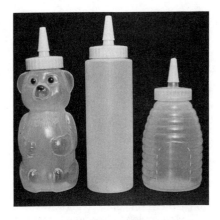

using earthenware, are very appealing, as are honey bears and exotic honey pourers.

Fill bottles to the proper level and avoid the offensive stickiness that results when bottles are over-filled. Set bottled and capped honey in a hot water bath to melt any remaining crystals, and clean jars of every last drop of stickiness. Consumers DO NOT LIKE sticky honey jars.

Labels

Labels on your honey containers should be attractive and eye-catching, but also allow the focus to be on the honey. The label should not hide the honey, and should be in a color that both complements the honey color and catches the eye. Crooked labels do not sell honey so always make them straight. They should show the net weight, name and address of the producer or packer and the principle floral source of the honey. If your name is not in the telephone directory, you must also put on your phone number. There are various rules regulating the information that must be on a label, and where it should be. Check with bee supply catalogs or your state inspector for more exact information.

If honey is being sold with little or no straining or heating, it may be labeled as "raw honey." An increasing amount of honey is being sold in this manner.

A small sticker with brief instructions for re-liquefying granulated honey should be attached to honey packed raw, since it may granulate before being used up.

Raw or Organic Honey

The demand for raw or organic honey has been slowly rising over the years. Both terms, when applied to honey are taken to mean honey that is not processed by fine filtering or straining, and not heated beyond the point required to liquefy it.

Honey sold as "organic" should be produced in an environment that is free of chemical residues and has been gathered from floral sources that are grown on soil free from chemicals or commercial fertilizers. It is not always possible to be sure of the "organic" character of honey. The term should be used carefully, as bees are rather indiscriminate when gathering nectar and do not necessarily avoid pesticide-treated areas. (Since nectar gathered from insecticide contaminated sources kill bees, chances are that no honey will be stored anyway.)

"Raw" honey implies that the honey is being sold in nearly the same condition that it comes from the extractor. Allowing honey to clear itself by settling in a tank at room tempera-

The best "raw" honey comes straight from the comb, like this section of comb honey. American Honey Institute Photo.

ture for one or more days will not alter the flavor or nutrient value of honey while still giving a good appearance in the bottle. The market for raw honey has been the exclusive province of the beekeeper-packer; use it to your best advantage by bottling only your best grades of honey.

Selling Comb and Chunk Honey

Honey from citrus, gallberry, mt. sage (California) and tupelo, and some others, are slow to granulate. Combs of these honeys should be used in comb or chunk honey production, to extend the shelf life. Package only as much as you can sell quickly; granulated combs look 'spoiled' to the consumer. Store all comb honey in the freezer until ready to sell.

Creamed Honey

When honey granulates quickly (high glucose/water ratio), the crystals are fine and closely packed. Slower granulation results in coarse, sand-like grains which many people find unpleasant to eat.

Some beekeepers specialize in **creamed** honey, which is a light and good flavored honey with tiny crystals, giving a creamy smooth consistency. Prof. E. J. Dyce worked on perfecting granulating honey. The method described below is the (patented) Dyce Process.

The result of this method not only produces fine-textured granulated honey, but also controls honey fermentation.

- Heat honey to 140°F (60°C) for 30 minutes or 160°F (71°C) for 1 minute (or somewhere between the two) to dissolve all sugar crystals and destroy yeast spores.
- Strain honey and cool to 75°F (24°C) rapidly. Make sure your containers are clean and dust-free.
- Add 5-10% (of total volume) starter crystals. This can be from your own honey or from an exceptionally fine store-bought creamed honey. It is better that these crystals were previously processed as described above.
- Stir in the seed crystals in such a way that no air bubbles are incorporated into the honey.
- After one to two hours, pack the honey in the final containers and store in a cold room (40°F, 4°C) for 12-24 hours to prevent any air bubbles from rising and giving the finished product a foamy look.
- Then place in an area maintained at 57°F (14°C) for 1-2 weeks. It should firmly set during this time and should maintain this creamy texture even at room temperature. If too hard, warm to 80-90°F (26-32°C) to soften.

Grading Honey

Honey is graded for color, flavor, moisture content and foreign material. The U. S. Dept. of Agriculture grades honey as Fancy, Choice, Standard and Sub-standard, but they are virtually never used.

Honey colors vary from water white to dark purple. The honeys of the Midwest and the Rocky mountain regions are generally lighter in color than those from the eastern United States and the South. No one has identified the actual ingredient that determines the colors of honey, but it relates to the kind of flower from which the nectar is taken.

Grading by **color** requires a device called a Pfund grader, it is used, as follows: (from E. Crane, "A Book of Honey", Oxford Un. Press, 1982).

	USA
water white	8mm
extra white	17
white	34
extra lt. amber	50
light amber	85
amber	114
dark amber	over 114

The U.S.D.A. also has a color comperator, a set of bottles filled with colored liquids, sorting the honey colors.

Flavor is exceeding difficult to define, and is mostly arbitrary. Most beekeepers use flavor associated with a particular flavor source, ie., orange blossom, clover, etc. Many consumers identify honey types by their distinctive flavors.

The aroma and flavor of honey are due to volatile materials. These are very difficult to identify. Besides color, the flavors of honeys are perhaps the most interesting property of this product. Certainly they distinguish honey from the manufactured syrups with artificial flavorings and colors.

Flavors are delicate and original to each flower, but they tend to become intermixed when being extracted. A strong and fairly sustained flow of nectar from acres of a single plant is necessary to give honey an identifiable flavor.

When different people are asked to describe the flavor of honey of a certain floral source, clover for instance, there is general agreement that the honey is mild, sweet and smooth. When asked to describe the flavor of a honey that has a more pronounced or distinctive flavor, the description becomes more different, as people taste the same thing differently.

Moisture content is measured by a refractometer which enables beekeepers to accurately calculate the percentage of solids in honey. Honey should not be more than 19% water or else it will begin to ferment.

Foreign matter usually means material other than pollen, unless the pollen content is too high. Dandelion honey is a good example. U.S.D.A. determines the presence of foreign material by straining Grade A honey (heated to 130°F (34°C)) through a #80 sieve (80 wire/inch). Some honeys with high pollen content are sold as "raw" or "evaporated" honey.

Honey As Food

Honey is a very complex food, the chemical composition of which varies according to the flower source. Other factors involving the flavor and quality of honey depend on the conditions under which it is gathered by the bees, processed, stored in the hive and in the honey house.

Honey is about 17-20% water. The largest proportion of dry matter in honey consists of the sugars **fructose** and **glucose.** These two sug-

Nothing tastes better than fresh baked bread covered with sweet comb honey.

ars occur in different proportions in honey. Together they make up about 85 to 95% of the carbohydrates of honey.

Nutrition/Medicinal Properties

Biologically, honey is anti-bacterial. There are three ways this comes about. First, researchers have found that during the ripening process enzymes such as **Inhibines,** are associated with the production and accumulation of hydrogen peroxide, a potent anti-bacterial agent. Second, its **acidity.** It ranges from 3.2 to 4.5 on the pH scale (vinegar is about 4.5). This makes bacterial growth difficult. The acidity also contributes to its flavor. A number of different acids are present, but the principal one is **gluconic,** produced by enzymatic action on the sugar dextrose (also known as glucose). The darker the honey the higher acidity. The acid-alkaline balance of the human body is dependent upon the mineral elements present; since the acids of honey are largely burned up during metabolism, honey is considered as an alkaline food.

And lastly, **osmotic pressure.** Because of its low water content (less than 18%) any moisture, whether from the air or from a bacterium, will be absorbed by honey. Such bacteria would die deprived of water. Since ancient times, honey has been successfully used to treat wounds because of its antibacterial activity.

While there are valuable nutrients in honey, the amounts are so small that eating it will not correct deficiencies. For children, old people and invalids, honey can be easily digested and is a palatable carbohydrate. Tests and clinical trials have shown honey to be readily assimilated by anyone. This, combined with the plain goodness of honey makes it a favorite addition to the diet. The only group that should not eat honey are young infants less than one year old.

Although enzymes in honey have no nutritive value in themselves, they play a very important part in the conversion of nectar sugars into ripened honey. **Diastase,** the starch-digesting enzyme, is present in very small quantities. It is added by the bees from their special glands during the "ripening" of the nectar, as is **invertase** another important enzyme. Both invertase and diastase are affected by heating honey.

Most, if not all of the vitamins found in honey are due to it's pollen content. The levels of vitamins are so low, however, that they have no nutritive significance.

The ash content of honey is less than 0.17%. Minerals present include potassium, sodium, calcium, magne-

Many foods taste better when honey is an ingredient. Kellogg Photo.

sium, iron, copper, manganese, chlorine, phosphorous, sulfur, silica and trace elements. The mineral content of darker honeys is higher.

In terms of calories, one teaspoon of honey contains 38 calories, (or 100 calories per tablespoon), one pound is 1380 calories (304 calories/100g).

Nevertheless, raw honey has much more to recommend it over the commercially manufactured syrups, such as corn syrup or **isomerose**, and syrup-honey blends. Careful handling of honey during harvesting, processing and storage is very important to preserve the physical, chemical and biological properties of this natural sweet.

Cooking with Honey

In general, honey can be substituted for sugar in any recipe, though some foods turn out better than others. Experiment first. Since honey is 17-20% water, the overall liquid in the recipe should be lowered.

If there is less than 2T sugar called for in the recipe, 2T honey can be used, eg. rolls, breads, muffins; (1 C equals 16 Tablespoons).

For cakes/cookies, substitute same amount sugar/honey but reduce the amount of liquid: 1/4 C for each 1 C honey used. For recipes:

If recipe calls for x C sugar	Use this much honey	Reduce liquid by
1/4 C sugar	1/3 C honey	1 T
1/3 C	1/2 C	2 T
1/2 C	2/3 C	3 T
2/3 C	1 C	1/3 C
3/4 C	1 C	1/4 C
1 C	1-1/3 C	6 T

Liquid in a recipe means water, juices, eggs or milk.

Some rules:
- for cakes with a less dense, better texture, use 50/50 sugar/honey.
- omit vanilla in honey cakes for better flavor.

- use a more moderate oven temp (350°-375°F) as honey darkens with too much heat.
- add an additional 1/12 - 1/5 t baking soda for every 1 C of honey used to counteract honey acids.
- if recipe calls for boiling the liquids, add honey after the liquids are boiled.

Measuring honey
- use greased utensil (like a spatula) so honey won't stick. Also, warmed honey will flow off and be less likely to stick.
- add honey gradually to eggs while beating, to prevent eggs from curdling.

Here is a handy guide to the sizes of jars and measurements in cups:

12 ounce bear	= 1 C
1 pound jar	= 1-1/4 C
2 pound jar	= 2-3/4 C
2-1/2 pound jar	= 3-1/2 C
3 pound jar	= 4 C
4 pound jar	= 5-1/2 C
5 pound jar	= 7 C

Honey Cakes, a comparison:

Ingred.	All Sugar	50/50	All Honey
cake flour	3 C	3 C	3 C
milk	1 C	13 T	10 T
shortening	1/2 C	1/2 C	1/2 C
sugar	1-1/2 C	3/4 C	—
honey	—	3/4 C	1-1/2 C
eggs	3	3	3
bak. pwd.	3 tsp.	3 tsp.	3 tsp.
vanilla	1 tsp.	—	—
salt	1/2 tsp.	1/2 tsp.	1/2 tsp.

Cream shortening and honey or sugar until light, add eggs one at a time, add sifted ingredients alternated with milk. Bake 350°F for 45 min. or until done. EXPERIMENT AND ENJOY!

Canning with honey
There are a few rules to remember when using honey in canning.

- use a larger kettle since honey foams up when boiling.
- if you use a 50/50 sugar/honey with jellies/jams, cook 7-9°F above temperature of boiling water (at your altitude).
- if using 100% honey, cook 10-12 degrees F above boiling water.

To make a honey syrup for packing fruits, no ascorbic acid is needed to retain fruit color.

- 50/50 sugar/honey with 4, 3 or 2 C boiling water (depending on sweetness of fruit) and boiled 5 minutes can be used to can fruits; 1 C syrup to 1 quart jar of fruit, and follow canning instructions.

Honey is a superior spread for breads and rolls. It has many other special uses such as in canning and freezing, as a sweetener for cereals, beverages, desserts and as a general cooking ingredient.

Honey can be used in candies, breads, cookies and bars, desserts (such as ices, creams, cakes and pies), jams and jellies, vegetables, salads and salad dressings, meat glazes, marinades, drinks, butters, snacks (granola, etc.), medicines, vinegars, wine, beer or mead. It also flavors some tobacco products, and is used in cosmetics.

Selling Beeswax

Beeswax has many uses, including cosmetics, food stuffs, water proofing, leather preparations, floor wax and pastes, sewing thread and in candle making and other crafts.

Cappings from extracted honey extraction make the best quality and whitest wax. Washed clean of honey and melted down, this wax can be sold at premium prices.

Darker combs should be melted separately and used in pastes or other products requiring lesser quality wax.

To prepare wax cakes for selling,

Blocks of wax ready to be made into useful products.

carefully strain wax to clear it of pollen, propolis and other foreign material. Do not overheat it, as it will darken. Pour into molds or small bread pans and place in a dust-free area to slowly cool. Once hardened, any impurities will settle to the bottom, and can be scraped off. To sell wax, make up cakes of different weights or sizes and wrap in clear plastic wrap. Store it in the freezer, as the wax moths will eventually find it! You can also make up batches of candles, leather or floor pastes, or sell the recipes along with the wax. Wax christmas ornaments can be made from candy molds and, of course, hand-dipped 100% beeswax candles are always popular.

Marketing

Most beginning beekeepers are interested in producing honey or other hive products, first, for their own use. If they have a surplus, they might look for ways to sell it. The biggest problem new or hobbyist beekeepers have is how to sell these products.

Marketing honey in large food stores is usually difficult for the beekeeper with only a few hundred pounds of honey to sell. Large grocery chains expect to buy from a supplier who can provide great amounts, consistently and of uniform color and flavor. These stores expect volume sales and a substantial margin of profit, two conditions which can only be met by those who buy, produce or pack large quantities of honey.

So, where do you start?

•**Fellow Workers or Neighbors:** This is an outlet that can be expanded by personal contact and other kinds of low cost promotion. To avoid embarrassment or other problems, be certain that selling it at work is allowed.

•**Retail Stores:** Small retail stores offer an opportunity to place your honey on display. Sales in case lots of retail-sized jars and other containers is the most convenient and profitable for the beekeeper. Christmas or other holidays is a good time to propose special packaging - ribbons, bows and candy canes make honey bears particularly popular.

•**Produce Stands:** This retail outlet continues to be popular with many beekeepers. A produce stand can draw both local and transient trade if located on a heavily traveled highway. This is an opportunity to sell your honey crop at the highest level of profit to you.

Observation hives at shows and flea markets do much to attract curious customers. Free literature and recipes are also appreciated.

A simple, but clean, honey stand near the highway attracts many customers.

•**Flea Markets, Farmer's Markets, Trade Shows, Fairs and other Public Events:** This type of sale takes advantage of a concentrated group of potential buyers. Direct retail sales at these events can be very heavy or light, depending on the interests and mood of the crowds. Again, take advantage of holiday decorations. Make use of a closed observation hive to draw in interested parties. A free honey recipe printed by your local county or state beekeeping organization will give resistant buyers a chance to try out cooking with this "new product".

Be careful though: As the demand for honey increases, there is a tendency to bottle honey from sources not up to standards the honey purchaser has come to expect. Poor grades of honey are usually set aside for bakeries which use honey of less than table grade. In addition, a certain amount of dark honey of a satisfactory flavor can be blended with light honeys of mild taste. The resulting blend yields a uniform product the year around, something that is difficult to achieve by the individual beekeeper.

Advertising

Nutrition is so important to our individual well-being that those who offer a first-rate product should not hesitate advertising its use, particularly when sold as pure, fresh, or in the comb.

Since honey absorbs water from the air, it is good to use it in baked goods. This quality keeps baked goods moist longer. Honey's unique or variable flavors can add a subtle taste to other foods made with honey, including beer, butter, vinegar, candy, ice cream and jelly.

Honey has an established market but it still needs continuous promotion. Honey and wax displays offer unlimited opportunities for artistic creations. Many beekeepers sell their honey right out of their houses.

Keep abreast of the activities of the National Honey Board, too. Their promotions, though large in scope, can aid you. Programs focus on cooking with honey, using honey in hot drinks, and enhancing the reputation of honey as a pure, natural product.

Good merchandising begins in the honey house by preparing a quality product. Simple displays of bottled honey can be placed conveniently near the front door when a customer calls. A little attention to the display and a friendly enthusiastic greeting is a good promotion. One note of caution: expanding home selling to a point where an outside sign is used will require you to check with your local zoning laws as well as your insurance company.

In summery, selling honey through the various channels of trade requires that your honey be in a presentable form which can be transported. Whether dispensed into customer's containers or already in retail containers, honey must be clean, good quality and the container suitably prepared for retail display and *not sticky*.

The alternative to selling your honey retail is to offer it at wholesale prices. Of course, not nearly as much work is involved in preparing the honey for market and the prices offered for bulk purchases are correspondingly lower.

11. Diseases and Pests of Honey Bees

Like all animals, honey bees are subject to a variety of diseases and pests. Fortunately, many of them can be controlled or cured. Only the most common disorders will be mentioned here.

If you think your bees have a brood disease, call in your local apiary inspector. If you have no local inspection service, notify your State Department of Agriculture. You may need to send them a sample of the comb on which disease is suspected. Follow their instructions carefully.

If you find a frame that looks like this, be suspicious, it may have a brood disease.

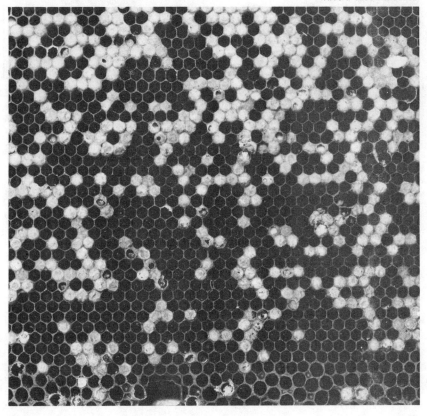

Brood Diseases

American Foulbrood (AFB)

Brood diseases are troublesome maladies that affect larvae and pupae. The most important of these is **American Foulbrood**, caused by a spore-forming bacteria, *Bacillus larvae*.

There are many characteristics of this disease that can be easily identified and will help you identify an AFB infection. The first outward sign will be sunken, discolored or perforated cappings. The larvae, which die after the cells have been capped, assume a coffee brown color. As the disease progresses, however, the larvae gradually decompose and become darker in color.

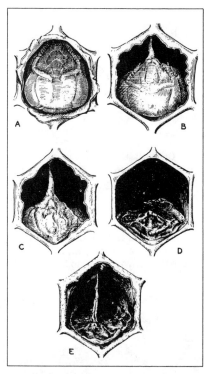

Bee pupa killed by American foulbrood: A-C, the heads of the pupa in progressive stages of decay; D-E, scales formed from the drying dead pupa. Notice the pupal tongue adhering to the side of the cell. USDA Handbook #335.

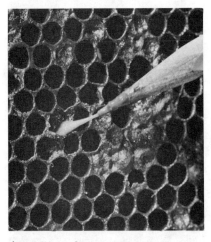

A positive characteristic of American foulbrood is the ropiness of dead larvae. The rope will snap back when stretched too far.

At this time the larvae exhibit a **ropy characteristic**. This is probably the most important diagnostic characteristic of the disease: the decaying larvae can be drawn out in a fine elastic thread which snaps back into the cell when broken. Of all the major brood diseases, *only* American foulbrood shows this characteristic.

After the larvae are completely destroyed, a **black scale** remains, which sticks to the bottom side of the cell. If there are many dead larvae, an unpleasant rotten odor is present.

The appearance of a "tongue" is another reliable sign of AFB, although this tongue is not always present. The appearance of the tongue results from *pupae* (not larvae) killed by the disease, which have decomposed in the same manner as the larvae. Occasionally the tongue of the pupa will adhere to the top side of the cell. When the disease is well-advanced, a characteristic rotting odor is present.

American foulbrood attacks primarily the worker brood, but in rare instances drone and queen larvae also become infected. The spores or dormant stage of AFB can contaminate another colony even after 50 years of storage in old equipment, wax or honey.

•Control Of AFB

It is essential to have a knowledge of the disease in order to diagnose an infection in its early stages. If it becomes advanced, the colony will be seriously weakened and robbing can occur. If robbers escape with infected honey they can spread the malady throughout the entire apiary.

It is generally conceded by most apiary inspectors that the cheapest and most effective way of controlling AFB is to destroy the infected colony. This is accomplished by killing the bees and burning them in a pit together with the contents of the hive, and covering the ashes with dirt. The hive bodies, top and bottom board are scorched with fire to sterilize them. This work should be done in cooperation with your apiary inspector or the beekeeping specialist from your state agricultural college.

Also, drugs can be used, but these may suppress the symptoms of AFB. Therefore, drugs should be fed only as a preventive and not a cure for American foulbrood. In the hands of an inexperienced or careless beekeeper, the feeding of drugs to infected colonies might only spread the disease.

Oxytetracycline (Terramycin™) antibiotic, is approved for use in treating American foulbrood. Formulations are available at bee supply stores. Terramycin is sold in varying strengths (grams per pound) which can be mixed with powdered sugar or fed as a syrup. TM 25 and TSP (terramycin soluble powder) should be fed

at the rate recommended on the package, or as follows: TM 25 -2 Tbl. in 20 Tbl. of powdered sugar. Use 3 Tbl. (1 oz), for feeding one colony.

For larger quantities, mix one pound of TM 10 and three pounds of powdered sugar. Place one ounce, or three level tablespoons of the medicated mixture on the top bars to the rear of the brood nest. Usually three dustings are required at four or five day intervals in the spring. Do not allow the powder to fall into cells containing larvae, as this will kill them. Administer the medication after the spring inspection and again in

---

Honey bee larva killed by European foulbrood. A, healthy larva at the earliest stage when it dies from EFB. B-C, a characteristic position of a diseased larva. D-E, longitudinal views of the scale that assumes a lengthwise position. USDA Photo.

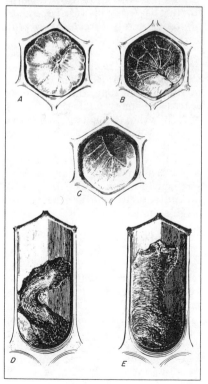

the fall, if necessary, after the honey is removed. Avoid giving any antibiotic at least *three weeks* before the main honey flow begins, to avoid having the medication stored in the surplus honey.

Terramycin is relatively unstable in honey and sugar syrup; it is best given as a powder.

European Foulbrood (EFB)

European foulbrood can be diagnosed by the appearance of the larvae, as they soon lose their plumpness and glistening white color. When infected, they turn grayish white to yellow. Later the decaying larvae turn from a light brown to a chocolate brown, and are found in almost any position in the cell. The characteristic symptoms are dead larvae coiled, or twisted in the cells.

EFB is also caused by a spore-forming bacteria called *Melissococcus pluton* (formerly *Streptococcus pluton*).

Scales of EFB are easily removed and there are never any tongues showing as in AFB. When decaying larvae become ropy, the ropiness is coarse and lumpy, while the ropiness of AFB is thin and elastic. When the disease is well along, a sour odor is evident.

EFB sometimes spreads rapidly and often an entire apiary will be stricken in a few weeks. It may be difficult to determine the source of the original infection.

•Control of EFB

Research has shown that terramycin will give good control of EFB when one part of TM-50 is mixed with 16 parts of powdered sugar. These materials should be mixed well with a flour sifter and then dusted on top of the frames in hive bodies containing brood. Four level tablespoons of the TM-50/powdered sugar mixture weigh approximately 34 grams, and

about 30 grams should be used to treat each colony.

A five-pound honey jar with large holes in the lid also makes a satisfactory duster for applying the powder. The colony should be dusted at weekly intervals until free of EFB. Three feedings should do it. Remember, don't let the powder get into open cells of larvae.

Attempts should be made to reduce any possible drifting in the apiary since drifting bees can spread EFB (and AFB). Windbreaks and low shrubbery will do a lot to help bees mark their locations and avoid drifting (see Chapter 8, Drifting).

Weak and badly diseased EFB colonies should be killed and removed from the apiary as these weak colonies may be robbed, permitting the disease organisms to be transferred to healthy colonies. EFB colonies that fail to respond to TM-50 treatment within a month should be destroyed.

Requeen your apiary with a strain of bees known to be resistant to AFB and EFB. Never breed from queens whose progeny have had EFB. This will help prevent the perpetuation of an EFB-susceptible strain.

Combs containing EFB scales should be melted and rendered for wax, and new foundation placed in the frames. It is now known that EFB scales will cause disease one year after being removed from a colony.

Feeding terramycin (TM-50) can greatly reduce the occurrence of EFB. Feeding these drugs should be started three weeks before the usual time for EFB to break out in your area. A second feeding should be given two weeks after the first. Consult your local apiary inspector or state agricultural agency.

Chalkbrood

Chalkbrood is a fungus disease that affects brood. It is caused by the fungus *Ascophaera apis* (Maassen ex

Claussen) which feeds on the larvae. The larvae turn from white to gray and black, becoming hard "mummies" which the bees discard. These mummies are often found on the bottom board. The disease is not usually considered serious, although it can be very damaging, especially in the spring or during wet summers. Maintaining strong colonies greatly reduces the incidence of chalkbrood disease.

You can also move hives to locations with good air drainage and sun exposure, add bees to strengthen weak colonies, or requeen.

Sacbrood

Sacbrood is a viral disease and cannot, therefore, be controlled by drugs. If your colony has sacbrood, many of the cappings will be perforated.

The gut of a healthy bee is shown below, clearly showing the segments. The diseased gut on the right is infected with Nosema. Abbott Labs Photo.

Tearing open these perforated cappings will reveal the larvae beneath with the following characteristics: The dead larvae lie on the bottom of the cell, with the head outward and extending upward. The tip of the head is generally black, while the rest of the body varies from gray to brown. The larvae can be easily removed intact from the cell and the whitish-gray stage at that time resembles a sac of water. The scales of this disease are dark brown to black and are easily removed from the cell. The turning up of the head and the whitish-gray sac are the two most distinctive characteristics of sacbrood.

There is no definite treatment for sacbrood. If your colonies show a high degree of infection, requeen the colo-

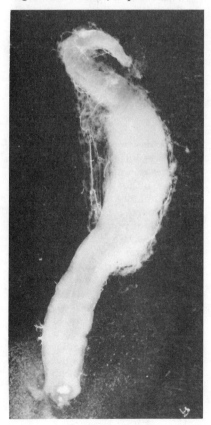

nies. In doing so, be sure the queens come from a different strain, especially one that is resistant to sacbrood. A good honey flow will also help clear it up.

Sacbrood is sometimes prevalent in the spring but it usually will decrease as the honey flow advances. It normally disappears without treatment at that time. Strong vigorous colonies are very effective in controlling this disease and requeening offers the best solution if the disease becomes serious.

Adult Bee Diseases

Nosema Disease

Nosema is the most widespread of all adult bee diseases, especially under northern climatic conditions where bees are confined for a long period of time. In the south, where colonies are able to fly almost every day, it is less frequently seen. Nosema is a disease which varies with the season and is usually worse during late winter and early spring. As the weather becomes warmer, the infection subsides and by July it is difficult to find any infected bees. The infection increases again as autumn approaches, although diseased bees are not as numerous as in the spring.

A microscopic protozoan, a single-celled animal called *Nosema apis* is the cause of nosema disease. Food or water can contain nosema spores and thus transmit infection.

When a colony is heavily infected with nosema, beekeepers observe their bees becoming increasingly restless and the colony becomes weaker. In the case of a light infection, the loss of bees may be so negligible as to go unnoticed. The queen is usually the last to die. Infected bees can be seen crawling on the ground, on the bottom board and at the entrance of the hive. The rear wings are usually at an

abnormal angle and the abdomen may appear shiny or greasy.

Do not confuse this disease with pesticide damage. Bees returning from fields freshly sprayed with poison will act in a similar fashion. However, nosema usually is most apparent in the spring, while pesticide poisoning usually occurs in mid to late summer.

•Treatment

Small stagnant pools of water help spread the disease. Provide bees with running water if they do not have access to a stream, or feed them clean water.

Fumagillin, sold under various trade names (Fumidil B), offers a method of controlling nosema.

A 9-1/2 gram bottle should be mixed with 50 gallons of 2:1 sugar syrup for spring feeding. The quantity may be reduced to proper proportions. Over-wintering colonies should be fed 1 or 2 gallons of medicated syrup, depending upon infection, climate, and food source. The spread of nosema in new packages can be reduced by feeding each colony a gallon of medicated syrup.

Pests of Bees

Wax Moth*

Although there are several species of moths that cause damage to stored combs, the greater wax moth, *Galleria mellonella* (L), is the most serious pest of combs and weak colonies. The larvae of this moth burrow into the combs after hatching from the egg, eating out the midrib of the comb.

There are three stages of the wax moth and all may be present simultaneously in the same hive. Development may be continuous except in northern climates where the temperature reaches freezing or below.

THE EGG. The egg of the moth is small (0.2 mm in diameter), white and slightly oblong. They are laid in masses or singly and are found in the cracks between hive parts (ie., between supers). In a strong colony, the female wax moth lays her eggs outside the hive. If the colony is weak, the eggs are laid inside the hive, farthest from the light. Bottom board hive debris is another good place to find them.

THE LARVAE. Eggs hatch into larvae (or worms) and it is in this stage that they are most destructive. (The egg, pupal and adult stages do no damage although their very presence is an impending threat for infestation). The larvae are whitish-gray, very small when first hatched, and very active. The length of the larval period ranges from 28 days to nearly 5 months, depending on the availability of food and the outside temperature.

These larvae eat the wax comb. And as they eat, they leave behind a silken tunnel full of droppings and wax debris. During this period, they grow from 1 to 1-3/8" (0.1 mm to 25 mm) in length. The rate of growth and the final size depends on the amount of impurities in the wax. The darker combs (eg., brood combs) have more impurities, such as cocoons, propolis, larval skins, and pollen, and have greater nutritional value. Foundation or lighter wax contains fewer impurities, and are seldom bothered.

Tunnels of the larvae can also be found in brood combs full of brood.

THE COCOON. When full grown, larvae spin a thick, rough silky cocoon. Some are found amid the web tunnels or in the waxy refuse on the bottom of the hive. More commonly, cocoons are firmly attached to some

Wax moths have virtually destroyed all the comb in this colony. The larval tunnels can be clearly seen on the right-hand frame. Cocoons cover the top bars and can be seen in the section super.

solid support, such as the sides of the hive. Sometimes the larvae chew directly into the wooden parts of the hive body or frame before spinning a cocoon. In more tropical areas, damage to wooden hive parts can be extensive, and controls are even more important.

THE PUPA. Within the cocoon, larvae change to pupae, and in 8 to 62 days an adult will emerge. The higher temperatures of 85°F (30°C) result in a shorter pupal stage; in the tropics, wax moths spend an average of 12 days as pupae.

THE ADULT. The normal size of an adult wax moth is 3/4 inch (20 mm) long with a wingspan of 1-1/4 inches (25-30 mm). The males are smaller than the females and their forewing has a scalloped margin, while females' wings are smooth. Adults are commonly seen resting on the comb

Adult wax moths seldom fly off, preferring to scurry across the comb. It holds it's wings to cover it's abdomen. H. Doering Photo.

with their wings folded over their abdomen like a roof. They are not easily induced to fly, preferring to scurry around on the comb if disturbed. Variation in their size and color is a result of food consumed and length of development period. Larvae that feed on dark brood combs tend to be dark gray or black adults.

The female mates inside the hive after emerging from the cocoon, and deposits her eggs 4-10 days later. She will continue to lay eggs as long as her vigor lasts. Egg laying may be rapid, and has been recorded at more than 100 eggs per minute. The total number of eggs varies, but is usually less than 300. The adult may live as long as three weeks, with the females living the longest.

*Contributed in part by Henry Mulzac

•Control

The greater wax moth will attack combs in weak colonies and gradually destroy them. Strong colonies are the best means of control, since a strong colony will destroy the moths and larvae.

Stored combs are very susceptible to wax moth injury, especially combs that have been used in brood rearing. Empty combs, wet or dry, can be stored successfully indoors or out in supers and hive bodies. The supers and hive bodies of combs should be stacked six high on a smooth pallet or metal cover. The joints between the supers, if not tight, should be taped all the way around with masking tape to make them airtight.

A cup of moth ball crystals, chemically known as **Paradichlorobenzene**, should be placed on a piece of cardboard and set on top of frames or combs in the top super. An empty shallow super should then be set on the top super, around the crystals and the stack covered with a tight cover and sealed with tape. The crystals emit a gas that is heavier than air and will seep down through the combs killing moths and worms, and protect the stack from future attacks. Crystals should be added to each stack of combs as they evaporate.

Before putting fumigated combs back on the hives, the stack should be broken apart and the combs aired outside for 72 hours.

There are chemicals available that control the larval stage of wax moth. Combs should be treated according to label instructions. Treatment can be expensive, but losing combs can be more expensive. Check bee supply catalogs for information.

Tracheal Mites

Acarine disease, known by its causative agent the tracheal mite, came into the United States from Mexico in 1984. The small mite (*Acarapis woodi* [Rennie]) lives inside the thoracic tracheae (breathing organs) of adult bees. A newly mated tracheal mite female emerges from an old host bee, and crawls up on the bee's hair and quests to find a newly emerged or callow bee. Once the mite finds a suitable host, she enters the trachea by means of the spiracle opening, and can lay 0.85 eggs/day for eight to 12 days (See chart). After the eggs hatch, the immature mites, or larvae, live as parasites inside all castes of adult bees, feeding on bee hemolymph or blood by piecing the walls of the tracheal tubes. New mites emerge 11-12 days (males) or 14-15 days later (females). Mites can cause severe bee losses, sometimes weakening or destroying entire colonies, especially in the north.

Controlling Tracheal Mites
Chemical Controls

Menthol crystals, from the plant *Mentha arvensis*, is sold in crystal or pellet form at many bee supply stores and each two story colony takes 1.8 oz. (50 g) of the menthol or one packet. The problem with menthol is that it is temperature dependent, and the odor will sometimes make bees leave the hive if the temperature is too hot, or be ineffective if the temperature is too cold. It should be in the colony at least two weeks. Remove all menthol at least one month before the surplus honeyflow to keep honey from becoming contaminated. As for all treatments, FOLLOW LABEL directions.

An alternate method is to use vegetable oil patties; a Crisco® and sugar patty (1:2 by wt.) kept on all the time protects against these mites. Terra patties also are beneficial in helping them overcome mite-vectored pathogens or other diseases.

Cultural Practices

Used with menthol or oil patties, these techniques help reduce the number of mites in a colony:
- Requeen colonies in fall.
- Reduce numbers of foragers & drones in fall by moving hives and destroying field force with soapy water.
- Place Terra patties on in the fall and spring; keep oil-only patties on during summer.
- If colony highly infested: split, kill older foragers, requeen, treat with menthol/oil.

Varroa Mites

First described and discovered in 1904 in Java, the varroa mite (*Varroa jacobsoni* Oudemans) was originally confined to Asia on *Apis cerana* or the Asian honey bee. As a result of man's moving mite-infested bees, varroa has spread since the late 1950s worldwide except Australia, New Zealand and Hawaii.

In 1986, varroa was first reported in the U.S. and is now one of the major

LIFE CYCLES OF THE TWO PARASITIC BEE MITES

TRACHEAL MITE (*Acarapis woodi* R.)

AGE OF BEE (*in Days*)

1 to 3 days	3 d	8 d	12 d

Female mite invades new 1-4 day old bee

Mite feeds and lays about 1 egg per day

Larvae emerge and feed. Females emerge in 14 days, males in 12. Mating occurs in the trachea

Daughter mites exit old host, quest on bee hair and transfer to a new, young bee host; enters trahcea

VARROA MITE (*Varroa jacobsoni* Oud.)

AGE OF BEE (*in Days*)

8 days	10 d	12 d	18 d	21 d

Female mite invades bee larvae about to be capped over

Mite hides in the bee brood food until cell is capped

When bee larva has spun its coccon, the mite feeds and begins to lay eggs

Mite lays up to five eggs which feed on developing bee. Mating occurs inside cell

Daughter mites exit when deformed bee emerges, Mites disperse to nurse bees and invade new cells killers of bee colonies. Adult female mites attach themselves onto adult bees and are carried to other uninfested colonies or apiaries. This method of transportation is known as phoresy.

Only adult female mites are found on adult bees, where they feed on bee hemolymph by piercing the soft tissues between segments or behind the head. Adult mites are about the size of a large pinhead and can be seen, with the unaided eye. Females are attracted to the odor of the drone brood pheromone—but they will also invade worker brood if there is not enough drone—and invade as the cells are about to be capped. There the mites hide at the bottom of the cell and emerge from the jelly after the pupa forms. The mite lays eggs on the pupa and young mites, or nymphs, feed on the hemolymph of pupa. Daughter mites mate with their brother in the honeycomb cells, after which the new females will emerge with the callow bee.

The new females will live for a time outside on other bees, until they invade new brood to repeat the cycle.

To date the only chemical control for varroa is Apistan® strips, a plastic strip (like a flea collar) impregnated with the pesticide Fluvalinate. Do not be tempted to use other materials, as some chemicals can become incorporated in the honey and wax, making them unfit for human consumption or sale.

Symptoms of Varroasis

- Infested capped drone or worker brood; cappings can be punctured, like foulbrood.
- Disfigured, stunted adult bees, with deformed legs and/or wings.
- Bees discarding larvae and pupae.
- Pale or dark reddish-brown spots on otherwise white pupae.
- Spotty brood pattern and the pres-

ence of diseases.
- Uncapped cells.
- General malaise of a colony.
- A dead colony in the early fall, right after honey has been harvested.

Detecting Varroa Mites

You can observe mites inside capped cells by using cappings scratcher (with fork-like tines) to pull up capped drone pupae. A heavy infestation is at least two mites per cell. The mites are clearly visible: Females are reddish brown and look tick-like on the white pupae. Immature mites are white or light brown. Other methods include the following:
1. Ether roll: (see diagram)
- collect approx. 200-300 bees in wide-mouthed jar with lid, from brood nest area. Do not capture the queen. Replace lid.
- knock bees to bottom of jar with sharp blow; there should be about 2 inch layer of bees on bottom of a quart jar.
- remove lid and spray 2 second burst with ether starter fluid.
- alternatively, add enough 70% alcohol, or soapy water to cover bees.
- if using ether, replace lid and agitate or roll jar for about 10 seconds; mites should stick to walls and appear as reddish brown spots on side of jar.
- if soap or alcohol was used, strain out bees with a coarse hardware cloth strainer, mites will be in the liquid.
2. Smoke or Strips plus Sticky Board
- place sticky board in bottom of colony; you can make one with cardboard or other stiff paper coated with Vaseline, tanglefoot or use a sheet of sticky shelf paper. Cut paper to fit bottom board.
- Smoke with 1 oz. pipe tobacco in smoker.
- puff bees 6-10 times, close up hive with rags for 10-20 min.

- Pull out sticky board after 10 min.
- Look for mites.
- Can also use Apistan® strips for up to 3 days with sticky board.

The damage varroa does to bees is subtle and still not clearly understood. Infested bees emerging from brood cells have:
- reduced flight activity
- 6-25% weight loss
- reduced life span (34-68%)
- reduced blood (hemolymph) by 15-50% when fed upon by mites
- external damage (chewed wings, legs, stunted growth) if <5 mites

Treatment for varroasis
- Keep strong colonies, disease free and well fed
- Apistan strips as per label instructions:
- Use 1 strip per 5 frames of bees; kills only varroa mites.
- Keep in colony for 42-56 days (one complete brood cycle); acts as a contact poison on external mites.
- Remove strips before supering for honey.

Bee Parasitic Mite Syndrome (BPMS)

First reported by European bee-keepers when colonies were stressed by varroa mites, BPMS was coined by researchers at the Beltsville Bee Lab, to explain why colonies infested with both mites are not thriving. BPMS may be connected to both parasitic bee mites vectoring a virus, called acute bee paralysis virus (ABPV), or other viruses. The symptoms can be present any time of the year and include:
- Varroa mites present in colony and usually tracheal mites
- Crawling bees on ground.
- Queens superseded more than normal.
- Brood pattern spotty, dead brood in all stages.
- Foulbroods and sacbrood *symptoms* present.
- AFB *symptoms* existing, but no ropiness, odor or brittle scales present.
- No predominant disease bacteria found.

Although not much is known

ETHER TESTING METHOD

STEP 1
- Remove 600 to 1000 bees from a center comb from the brood nest. Place into a quart jar.
- Place lid on jar, tap jar to settle bees to bottom.

STEP 2
- Using a can of aerosol ether-based starter fluid (used to start cars in cold weather), spray into jar for approx. 1 (one) second.
- Close jar immediately and gently shake/roll bees for 15-20 seconds.

STEP 3

- Then, turn jar on it's side and gently roll bees.
- Any mites present will adhere to the film left on the sides of the jar.
- Mites will be about the size of a common pin head, and a bright, medium to dark brown color.
- If you suspect mites to be present, empty the bees and rinse the film with 70% (rubbing) alcohol. Take, or send, to your local inspector.
- Remember, this test is NOT foolproof. You need to check SEVERAL colonies in your apiary. Also, very low infestations will not show up on this test.

Drawings courtesy of Oregon State University.

about BPMS, these treatments may be effective:

- Feed colonies with Terra in syrup; feed with fumigillan.
- Treat for varroa with Apistan Strips.
- Treat for tracheal mites with extender or vegetable oil patties.
- Feed pollen supplements.

Management Strategies for Both Mites

If a colony is highly infested with both mites, try this:

- Split, kill older foragers, requeen, treat with recommended remedies
- Provide food supplements, protein and carbohydrates if needed

If both mites are present, plan for spring and fall treatments using these guidelines:

Spring:

- Feed colonies pollen supplement, or substitute
- Treat with Apistan® Strips; take off in 42-56 days
- Treat with oil-sugar patties, renew as needed
- Feed as needed

Summer: keep oil-only patties on during summer.

Fall:

- Requeen colonies in fall and reduce numbers of old foragers
- Place extender patties on in the fall (treat with menthol)
- Early in fall, harvest honey supers
- Reduce numbers of foragers & drones in fall
- Move hives and destroy field force
- Treat with Apistan® Strips and fumigillan
- Take off strips after 45-56 days, DO NOT LEAVE IN ALL WINTER
- Treat with oil-sugar-TM patties
- Use resistant bee stock. Hygienic behavior seems to be beneficial for varroa mite control and some bees appear to pick off the mites.

Integrated Pest management (IPM) strategy uses multiple tactics such as requeening, chemical, and soft controls to "manage" the mites instead of killing all of them, provided they do not damage the hive. Remember, it is not possible to kill all mites in a hive and all mites in a region. The presence of some mites in the hive does not detract from hive health, provided the colony is strong and that mite numbers do not get out of hand. Biological controls:

- restrict brood rearing by caging queen, removing capped brood
- treat adults to kill mites
- trap mites in drone-comb brood (freeze)
- special plastic frames can be used — ANP Bee Comb Inserts®

Africanized Bees

Be alert for the migration of the **"Africanized"** honey bee into your region. This bee, accidentally released in Brazil is more aggressive than domestic European bees. Extensive work is being done to determine how far north this bee can survive, what its influence on hobby and commercial beekeeping might be, and methods of managing or genetically controlling this insect. As of 1997 it was already in TX, NM, AZ and CA.

Ants

Several species of ants invade beehives but if the colony of bees is of normal strength and given free access to all areas of the hive, they will usually be able to repel the ants.

You can discourage ants from invading hives by using kerosene and diesel oil applied to the ground around the hive. Avoid an excess which may cause harmful fumes. This will give temporary control.

If ants are especially bad, hive stands with legs in cans of oil may give a more permanent deterrent.

Mice cause more damage than is appreciated by many beekeepers. This nest was placed between the frames, where the mice can chew on combs at leisure. R.V. Roberts Photo.

Fire ants, commonly found in the south (but moving west), can cause considerable damage to even a strong hive. Control measures are often ineffective, and moving an apiary may be your only recourse. Contact state extension agents concerning controls.

Mice

In the fall, mice find beehives a cozy place to spend the winter. This might not be bad, but they insist on chewing up the comb and bringing in nesting materials.

To prevent this, close off the lower entrance to your hive with an entrance reducer that mice won't be able to chew through. Talk with beekeepers in your area about how they control mice. Use wire mesh to close entrance to mice, but allow bees to pass through.

12. Beekeeping Social Skills

Keeping Bees in Residential Areas

Beekeeping has become a very popular hobby, one which can bring enjoyment to every age, whether you live in a city, village or on a farm. Honey bees are not difficult to care for as the only housing they require is their hives. But they do need room to fly freely to and from their hives. Place them as far as possible from the property boundaries with your neighbors; away from patios, gardens, swimming pools, walks or other public thoroughfares. Most people who keep bees as a hobby want only a few hives and would prefer to keep them in their backyard. Out of concern for the rights of neighbors to enjoy their own yards, every beekeeper must carefully observe these practices of bee management that will minimize unnecessary disturbances to the hives. Bees become defensive when they feel threatened or are mishandled, and they could easily become a nuisance to your immediate neighborhood if so treated.

Points to Consider

•**Obtain Gentle Bees.** A number of breeders offer gentle strains of bees noted for being calm and easy to work. These are usually Caucasian or Carniolan bees. Requeen each fall with such queens.

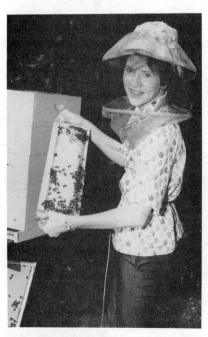

Obtain bee races or strains that are gentle to handle.

•**Keep your bees out of sight, if possible.** This reduces vandalism. Your neighbors may have an abnormal fear of honey bees if they have seen one of the "Killer Bee" scare movies.

•**Don't work bees if your close neighbors are outdoors.** This may not always be possible but it reduces the chance of problems.

•**Don't over-populate your lot with**

115

bees. One to two colonies is plenty for a 1/4-1/3 acre residential lot. Later you may feel you could add to that depending on the circumstances.

Hide your hive behind a fence or hedge. Work your bees only on calm, sunny days.

•**Learn to keep your bees calm.** Open your hives only when the weather is warm and sunny and there is a nectar flow. Smoke the entrance a few minutes before opening the cover.

It is important to keep weeds down in front of your hives. But remember, this can aggravate the bees. Mow when bees are in the hives (late afternoon) or when there are few neighbors outside.

On cold, cloudy days, the bees will be more irritable than on sunny, warm days. Try to work during the middle of the day — between 10 a.m. and 2 p.m. if possible. If grass must be mowed in front of your hives, avoid directing the stream of air and grass into the hive entrances.

•**Use swarm prevention management.** New swarms are usually no hazard but they tend to unnerve neighbors who don't understand bees. Read up on swarm prevention. If your bees do swarm, use it as an opportunity to convince the residents that you are a skillful, knowledgeable beekeeper.

•**Keep the line of flight well above your neighbor's property.** Bees should be at least 7 feet high as they cross your neighbor's property line. Provide a barrier such as shrubs, fences or buildings which they must fly over. Don't put your hives closer than 10 feet to neighbors property.

•**Provide a Continuous Source of Water.** Bees can become a nuisance at local swimming pools. If you provide a continuous source of water this is less likely to happen. One way is to let an outside water tap drip onto a board. Another way is to use a Boardman Feeder continually filled with water. (A chicken waterer works well if you fill the bottom with coarse gravel so the bees won't drown.) The bees become accustomed to gathering water at this point and are less likely to seek it from pools and other exposed sources around the neighborhood.

•**Sweeten up your neighbors with some honey.** Getting along with the folks next door takes some effort but it can save you a lot of grief. Giving them a jar of honey occasionally gives you an opportunity to point out the importance of your bees in pollinating the local fruit trees and vegetable gardens.

•Other Points to Remember

There are many conditions which can cause bees to become troublesome. Not all are the fault of the beekeeper. But it is your responsibility to become familiar with the circumstances which may result in stings or annoyance to your neighbors.

• Work with your bees with slow, deliberate movements. Avoid crushing bees when opening and closing the hives and when handling combs. Use smoke sparingly.

• Avoid situations that can lead to robbing. Do not allow combs of honey to be exposed when there is no nectar being gathered. Robbing causes a very serious disturbance and is difficult to stop once it begins. If your bees must be fed, use combs of honey. If syrup is being fed, be certain that only the bees in the colony being fed have access to the syrup.

Know Your Bees

Anything that makes you a better beekeeper makes you a better neighbor as well. As you become more proficient with bees, it will be reflected in the confident manner you handle the problems that may arise with your neighbors. Information about bees and beekeeping may come from the following:
1. Bee suppliers have free information pamphlets and catalogs on request. Books on beekeeping may be purchased or borrowed, and you can subscribe to a monthly beekeeping magazine.
2. Join a beekeeping organization. Learn who is likely to give you the best advice. Friendships made by being a member can be a valuable aid if you need assistance in resolving problems you may encounter with beekeeping ordinances or hostile neighbors.
3. The United States Department of

Agriculture, your state Cooperative Extension Service or your State University usually have publications and consultation services at your local level. Your County Agricultural Agent has information on these agencies and where to secure the publications.

Correspondence courses are offered through some of the Agricultural colleges. Nearly every state has a State Apiarist who has charge of a team of apiary inspectors, usually experienced professionals who will check your bees periodically for disease. Their advice may be sought if it is in line with their inspection services.
4. Your best instruction is your own experiences, but do not let this keep you from seeking advice on bees and their management especially in matters that may turn into problems with your neighbors. You will usually find among your fellow beekeepers some who have experienced similar circumstances. No matter how they handled their problems you can profit from their experience if you consider it in light of your own good judgment.

Ordinance Problems

Anyone contemplating keeping bees in a residential neighborhood should carefully check for any restrictions which apply to bees. If you find that an outright ban is in effect, you have no choice but to begin your beekeeping at a location outside the restricted area. Locations for bees can often be found in rural areas and they may have the advantage of being better honey producing sites. Some local restrictions limit the number of hives that may be kept on a city lot and include certain requirements for placement and maintenance. These may include: maintaining the hives a certain number of feet away from lot lines, protective fences which force bee flights high, and keeping a constant source of water available for the bees.

If no restrictions are in effect, you must share in the responsibility of keeping bees in a manner that reflects well on all beekeepers in your community. This is the best guarantee that no problems between bees and people will become so acute that controls or bans on beekeeping will be asked for in your community.

Unfortunately, some neighbors will not be reassured that bees can be kept near their home, and you may be forced into some manner of confrontation in spite of all the efforts you have made to avoid it.

As a beekeeper, you have responsibilities to your neighbors. It also gives you opportunities to be friendly and understanding with those who are not familiar with bees, and may fear for their own or their children's safety. Keep a low profile with your bees. It may give you pleasure to look out your window at a well-ordered row of busy hives, but to your neighbor it may be very frightening. Locate the hives as far as possible from high traffic areas and if necessary, shield them with solid rows of live hedges which can also be an attractive nectar-bearing plant. If a flight line diversion is needed immediately, a semi-solid fence may be constructed of wood. Keep it attractive and only as high as necessary to cause the field bees to come and go at a steep angle at the front of the hive. Having a barrier also limits the area to within a short distance of the hive entrance that guard bees consider critical to their defense and beyond which they are unlikely to attack and sting.

Gifts of honey will please many neighbors and tend to ease some of the tensions that may build up. Do this as a friendly gesture and not as a bribe. Patience and understanding with people is as necessary to learn as the art of working with bees.

•If You Are Cited

Despite all your best efforts, you may come into conflict with very persistant opposition and will be given a summons to appear before a Magistrate or a hearing body in your community. Hearing of the specific complaints should call for an immediate appraisal of your position in relation to any violations which you may have overlooked or of which you were unaware concerning your bees. Have a lawyer assist you with a frank appraisal of your position in regard to both your beekeeping and your legal rights.

If you have the least doubt as to your position or the processes in which you will be involved, such as testifying and answering questions, it would be wise to hire legal counsel.

Even with legal assistance, do not neglect to prepare yourself in other ways. Secure letters and circulate petitions to reinforce your stand. Invite some of the respected, cooler heads of the community, all the better if they are also beekeepers or sympathetic to your hobby, to come to the hearing. Someone with a short temper can be more harm than help.

The public officials are interested in hearing both sides of the issue presented factually and without exaggeration. Do your homework. Here, your testimony may be more valuable than that of your attorney. Keep your statements to the point in answering questions about your beekeeping. Do not assume the hearing officers have made up their minds. They are usually trying to find a middle ground to keep both parties happy. Do not be argumentative. Do not quote obscure bee lore and do not make statements that may appear irrational to someone unfamiliar with bee behavior.

Be reassuring about the safety of properly cared for bees such as yours; but do not promise that no one will ever be stung by your bees. Now is a good opportunity to make the point that banning beekeeping in the community will not guarantee this either because there are bees in hollow trees as well as other stinging insects.

If the question is an ordinance banning bees, you might respectfully point out that dogs can bite and cats can scratch but they are not banned. You can explain that in general, the public has difficulty identifying the difference between a honey bee, yellow jacket and a hornet. The latter two are much more aggressive and apt to sting, but the honey bee often gets blamed.

Undoubtedly the question of people dying from allergic reactions to bee stings will come up. Some people are allergic to bee stings just as some people are allergic to cats, pollen or antibiotics. An allergic reaction to a sting may involve the sudden onset of dizziness, nausea, perspiration, or shortness of breath.

How common are allergic reactions to bee stings? The best medical evidence indicates that fewer than two people out of 1,000 are allergic to honey bee stings. More people are allergic to wasps and ants than honey bees.

Sensitivity to antibiotics cause more deaths each year than honey bees, but no reasonable person would consider banning their use because of their benefit to mankind.

In bee sting allergy, the first sting sensitizes and the second causes the allergic reaction. Just as the person with heart disease has the responsibility to seek medical help, the person with a sting allergy has the responsibility of seeking an allergist to be desensitized.

With a small blood sample an allergist can determine quite quickly whether a person is sensitive to the most common types of insect stings.

The importance of bees should also be stressed. In addition to provid-

Bees are important pollinators of crops such as this onion flower. D. Sammataro Photo.

ing honey and beeswax, bees provide millions of dollars in pollination service in the U.S. annually by pollinating over 90 agricultural crops.

These are crops such as apples, cherries, strawberries, radishes, cucumbers, carrots, etc. The pollen from these blossoms is heavy and oily so wind pollination is not possible.

The job of pollination of urban gardens and fruit trees falls more heavily on the honey bee each year, due to the widespread use of pesticides and the lack of nesting sites in the city environment for other types of pollinating insects.

There will be conflicting statements from those giving testimony but it may not be permitted for you to challenge testimony made during the hearings, unless you have an attorney. Your best defense is to give clear, concise answers to questions, rely on friendly, credible testimony from people familiar with your circumstances and, if using attorneys, leave it to them to guide your case in the best possible manner.

• How To Adjust To Alternatives

It is possible that the ruling may go against you. You may be assessed certain costs and whatever penalties are due as a result of being in violation of an ordinance. This must be paid. To avoid further citations, your bees must either be moved out of the restricted area or immediate steps must be taken to bring them into conformance with the conditions of the regulatory ordinance.

If your home apiary must meet certain standards of maintenance to be legally approved, do your best to meet and maintain these standards. Failure to do so will reflect not only on you but on other beekeepers in your community. In many instances where beekeeping has been banned or severely restricted, it has been the result of having one or more thoughtless beekeepers who stubbornly refused to alter their manner of keeping bees, when it was apparent to everyone, including other beekeepers, that they were conducting activities in a manner offensive to everyone around. Heedless of advice, the uncooperative beekeeper may bring a crisis not only on themselves, but on those who are making an honest effort to keep bees in a manner befitting a good citizen of the community.

Organizing a Bee Association

Beekeeping, like any other activity, attracts a number of people with similar interests who want to meet on a regular basis. A bee meeting, part social, part educational, is an important opportunity to learn and share experiences and ideas with others. Starting up an organization, however, can result in disappointment if some simple rules are not followed from the start. We hope that the suggestions listed here will make your beekeepers association a successful and long-lasting one.

Getting Started

First of all, you must select some people to become the organizing committee. They should be beekeepers, both experienced and new, who are interested in forming an association. Elect a committee leader and discuss and choose the following:

1. **A name for the Association.**
2. **The date and frequency of meetings.** Investigate where your meetings can be held: a church basement, school or county extension auditorium. How much it will cost will help determine your annual dues.
3. **The amount of annual dues.** Collect them at the *first* meeting so your group has some working capital.
4. **How to publicize your meetings.** Choose one or two people to be the official "speakers" of your group to the media; this includes local and regional newspapers, radio and television stations and county or state agricultural agencies.
5. **A nominating committee.** They will arrange for the election of officers: president, vice-president, secretary, treasurer, and program chairperson. A board of directors may be organized later as the association grows.
6. **A recording system for the meetings.** This can be a person who knows shorthand, or owns a tape cassette recorder. Written records of the minutes of the meetings *must be kept.*
7. **A checking or savings account.** Someone who has had bookkeeping experience should be the treasurer.
8. **A set of rules and by-laws.** Copies of by-laws can be obtained from other groups. Most often,

Roberts Rules are the guideline used. These can be modified to suit your particular needs.

9. **A newsletter.** Will your group be big enough to afford publishing their own newsletter? Who will write it?

10. **Date of first meeting, to elect the officers.** Roberts Rules of Order is generally the parliamentary proceedings used, although a less formal structure can be used.

11. **Make your programs interesting and varied.** The program chairperson should find out what the members want to hear and select speakers and programs accordingly. If the members are mostly new to beekeeping, then the first year should concentrate on improving skills, introducing new techniques, or updating information on pests and diseases. This can be done through using videos, movies or inviting guest lecturers. Barbecues or honey tasting contests are good ways of learning to cook with and sell honey.

• The Members

Your organization must benefit as many individuals as possible if it expects to maintain attendance and grow.

If your group has mostly experienced beekeepers, organize trips to State University Bee Labs or schools, or a local honey packer or commercial apiary. Write information packets or true/false quizzes to distribute to schools. Visit each other and discover new techniques for queen rearing, swarm management, or honey production.

Attracting new members should be a priority if you want your organization to grow. This can be done by word of mouth; have each member bring a new guest at least twice a year.

Another way is to publicize your meetings in the local papers. This should be done on a regular basis, in case someone needs a beekeeper to pick up a swarm, or answer questions about African bees, etc. Learn how to write an effective news release (see below).

Appoint somebody before each meeting who's job it will be to greet new and old members and guests *at the door*. Sometimes, this is all you need to break the ice. Make sure all the beekeepers in your area are invited. Some may not read the papers or see the notices; a personal phone call from the President or other officer is a good way to encourage participants otherwise reluctant to attend.

One way to locate beekeepers in your area is to contact the local or state inspector for names and addresses of known beekeepers. They are usually cooperative because in the long run, an educated beekeeper will make their job easier.

• Benefits of Belonging

Belonging to associations of any kind, whether it be beekeepers, pigeon racers or computer programers, can benefit you in many ways:

• You get to know other people with similar interests, in this case other beekeepers.

• Through the programs, you become better educated in your field, and perfect the skills needed to make beekeeping more enjoyable or more profitable.

• Your group can play an important role in the community by educating the public on the importance of bees. Be involved in the local issues relating to bees and become the authority.

• Your group or its representatives, can be involved on a state and national level with other state beekeeping organizations. In this way, your group can keep up with

An impressive honey display at a state fair will help people appreciate bees.

current happenings with the problems that affect you: Africanized Bees, Varroa or Tracheal Mites, Diseases, government programs and national policies relating to beekeeping.

• Your group could also play an important part in advancing the art of beekeeping to others. Rotate selected members to appear at 4-H, church or school groups; actively participate in county and state fairs or other functions. In this way, not only your group, but beekeeping in general will appear in a positive way to the public eye.

• Members can cooperatively purchase equipment, bees or journal subscriptions at a reduced rate.

• Fund raising drives are easy to organize, since your group already has an infrastructure. Hold honey/ bake sales or similar sales to raise money. A 100-member garage sale could be quite an event!

• The Future of Your Organization

In order to maintain your membership, a person or committee should devote full time to solicit new members. This not only insures the future of your group, but a future for beekeeping in general. Only by recruiting new members and keeping in the public eye will your group continue.

Besides talking to school or other groups, hold an annual festival or essay contest. Choose a student winner each year and have as an award a complete beginners outfit and a year's free training with an experienced beekeeper. You can always include a reclamation clause to get back the equipment/bees if the participant should quit. But you also could interest many school-age students who are potential, future beekeepers.

Write articles for local newspapers or have a yearly Bee Bash open to the public where you give out door prizes and free literature. If you don't want to write your own, reproduce an article from a bee journal (give credit please) or write to bee companies. Many of the latter have free literature to use as handouts. Remember, an

Future beekeepers should have their natural curiosity encouraged by bee groups or in schools. G. F. Townsend Photo.

organization exists only as long as it has members. A beekeeping association can provide the setting for the novice or the well-informed beekeeper to exchange ideas and experiences while providing a community service that benefits everybody.

How to Write a Press Release

Maintaining good relations with local and regional newspapers is probably the most cost-efficient and productive means a small organization has to promote themselves and recruit new members. But to communicate effectively, and at the same time attract new members requires following some simple guidelines.

Your news release must contain all of the information needed to tell your story. Specifically:

WHO: The Brown County
         Beekeepers Association
WHAT: Will hold their fall
         meeting
WHERE: In the basement of the
         Town Hall
WHEN: On Friday, Sept. 9, 1988
         at 8:00 p.m.
TOPIC: Mr. Bill Curtis will speak
         on winter preparations
         for bees
MISC.:   Every one is welcome.
         Refreshments will be
         served. No fee to attend.

If you supply this basic information, your press release will read something like this:

BEEKEEPERS MEET. On Friday, September 9th at 8:00 p.m. The Brown Co. Beekeepers Association will meet to discuss winter preparations. The meeting will be in the basement of the Town Hall. Refreshments will be served. Everyone is welcome.

However, with just a little imagination, you can prepare the same information in a much more entertaining and attractive format. Such as:

DO BEES SHIVER ALL WINTER? Find out on Friday, September 9th, 1988, when expert beekeeper Bill Curtis will discuss honey bees and wintering, and what beekeepers can

do to help. The meeting will be held in the basement of the Town Hall, and there is plenty of free parking in the back. The Brown County Beekeepers Association invites any and everyone to find out if bees really do shiver all winter. They'll have free refreshments afterwards, and look forward to seeing you there.

If possible, deliver this announcement in person, so you get to know who is in charge of these types of notices, and they in turn will get to know you. This type of contact can be invaluable when you need help, or when a newspaper wants to talk to a knowledgeable beekeeper.

Epilog

This book is certainly for anyone interested in the fascinating world of the honey bee. But if your discoveries have led you to the world of beekeeping, or you have already embarked on this exciting adventure, we welcome you to one of the most select groups in the field of agriculture.

With this book, you have all the tools necessary to take your first steps in this activity. But we encourage you to increase your knowledge and skills by using the references we've listed, subscribe to appropriate periodicals and practice, practice, practice.

But most importantly, we cannot overemphasize the necessity of being a 'social' beekeeper. Joining local, state and national associations will help you pursue the latest in beekeeping skills and information. Becoming involved in these groups will not only aid them with a pair of hands to lighten the load, but will teach you skills you can learn in no other way.

Beekeeping — a hobby, a pastime, a career — no matter what your goals, an activity you can grow with.

Glossary

A

ABDOMEN: The posterior or third region of the body of the bee that encloses the honey stomach, stomach, intestines, sting and the reproductive organs.

ACARAPIS WOODI: A mite, called the Tracheal mite, which infests the bees' breathing or tracheal system; sometimes called Acarine Disease, this refers to bees that are heavily infested with the Tracheal mite.

ACIDITY: The state of being acid or sour; the acids in honey, called organic acids, include gluconic acid, formed by the enzyme glucose-oxidase which works on glucose to produce the acid and hydrogen peroxide.

AFTERSWARM: Swarms which leave a colony with a virgin queen, after the first (or prime) swarm has departed in the same season; afterswarms are also referred to as secondary or tertiary swarms.

AFRICANIZED BEE: A term used indiscriminately to describe the African honey bee *Apis mellifera scutellata* (formerly *A.m. adansonii*) or its hybrids; an African bee released in Brazil and known for its volatile nature, its aggressive behavior may cause concern to the non-beekeeping public.

ALARM ODOR: A chemical (iso-pentyl acetate) substance released near the worker bee's sting which alerts other bees to danger; also called alarm pheromone.

ALLERGIC REACTION: A systemic or general reaction to some compound, such as bee venom, characterized by itching all over (hives), breathing difficulty, sneezing or loss of consciousness.

ANTHER: From the Greek *anthros* (flower), referring to the pollen-bearing portion resting on top of the stamen or male part of a flower.

ANTENNA (pl -AE): One of two long segmented sensory filaments located on the head of the bee, which enable bees to smell and taste.

APIARY (pl -IES): The location and total number of hives (and other equipment) at one site; also called bee yard.

B

BALLING: Refers to the action of worker bees surrounding a queen who is unacceptable, they are trying to kill her by pulling her legs, wings, and by stinging and suffocation; the bees form a small cluster or ball around this queen.

BASKET EXTRACTOR: A honey extractor that spins out one side of the frame at a time.

BEE BLOWER: A gas or electrictrically driven blower used to blow bees from supers full of honey.

BEE BREAD: Pollen collected by bees and stored in wax cells, preserved with honey.

BEE BRUSH: A soft brush or wisk (or handful of grass) used to remove bees from frames.

BEE CELLAR: An underground room used for storing bee hives during long cold winters; difficult to use as constant temperature and humidity must be maintained to ensure colony survival.

BEE DISEASES: Diseases affecting adult or larval honey bees, not all of which are infectious (such as dysentery); important diseases are American and European foulbrood, highly infectious larval diseases.

BEE ESCAPE: A device constructed to permit bees to pass one way, but prevent their return; used to clear bees from supers or other uses.

BEE GO: A chemical, such as benzaldehyde, repellent to bees and used with a fume board to clear bees from honey supers.

BEE SPACE: A space big enough to permit free passage for a bee but too small to encourage comb building, and too large to induce propolizing activities; measures 1/4 to 3/8 inch (9.5mm).

BEE SUIT: A pair of coveralls, usually white, made for beekeepers to protect them from stings and keep their clothes clean; some come equipped with zip-on veils.

BEESWAX: A complex mixture of organic compounds secreted by four pairs of glands on the ventral, or underside of a young worker bee's abdomen, secreted as droplets which harden into scales, they are used to construct honey comb; melting point of beeswax is 143.6-149°F (62-65°C).

BEEWAY SUPER: The shallowest or section super used with wooden section boxes to make comb honey; has a built-in beeway or bee space.

BLACK SCALE: Refers to the appearance of a dried down larva or pupa which died of a foulbrood disease.

BOARDMAN FEEDER: A wooden or plastic device that fits into the entrance of a bee hive and holds a quart jar that can be filled with syrup or water.

BOTTLING TANK: A plastic or stainless steel tank holding 5 or more gallons of honey and equipped with a honey gate to fill honey jars.

BOTTOM BOARD: The floor of a bee hive.

BROOD: Immature stages of bees not yet emerged from their cells; the stages are egg, larvae, pupae.

BROOD DISEASES: Diseases that affect only the immature stages of bees, such as American or European foulbrood.

BROOD NEST: The part of the hive interior in which brood is reared; usually the two bottom supers.

BUCKFAST HYBRID: A strain of bees developed by Brother Adam at Buckfast Abbey in England, bred for disease resistance, disinclination to swarm, hardiness, comb building and good temper.

BURR COMB: Small pieces of comb made as connecting links between combs or between a frame and the hive itself; also called brace comb.

C

CAGE, SHIPPING: Also called a package, a screened box filled with 2 to 5 pounds of bees, with or without a queen, and supplied with a feeder can; used to start a new colony, or to boost a weak one.

CANDY PLUG: A fondant type candy placed in one end of a queen cage to delay her release.

CAPPED BROOD: Immature bees whose cells have been sealed over with a brown wax cover by other worker bees; inside, the non-feeding larvae are isolated and can spin cocoons prior to pupating.

CAPPINGS: The thin wax covering over honey; once cut off of extracting frames they are referred to as cappings and are a source of premium beeswax.

CAPPINGS SCRATCHER: A fork-like device used to remove wax cappings covering honey, so it can be extracted.

CARBOHYDRATE: A food (organic compound) composed of carbon, hydrogen, and oxygen $(CH_2O)_n$, with the hydrogen:oxygen ratio frequently 2:1, as in water H_2O.

CARNIOLAN BEES: A grayish race of honey bee *Apis mellifera carnica* named for Carniola, Austria but originating in the Balkan region; while they are gentle and do not propolize, they tend to swarm more than other races.

CAUCASIAN BEES: A black race of honey bee *A. mellifera caucasica,* originating in the Caucasus mountains; gentle but tend to propolize excessively.

CHALKBROOD: A disease affecting bee larvae, caused by a fungus *Ascosphaera apis,* larvae eventually turn into hard, chalky white "mummies".

CHIMNEY EFFECT: The tendancy for bees to fill only the center frames of honey supers; happens when bees are given too much room too fast.

CHROMOSOME: A group of nuclear bodies (from the nucleus) containing genes; responsible for the differentiation and activity of a cell, and undergoing characteristic division stages such as mitosis.

CHUNK HONEY: Honey in the comb, but not in sections, frequently cut and packed into jars then filled with liquid honey.

COCOON: A thin silk covering secreted by larval honey bees in their cells in preparation for pupation.

COMB: The wax portion of a colony in which eggs are laid, and honey and pollen are stored.

COMB, DRAWN: Wax foundation with the cell walls drawn out by the bees, completing the comb.

COMB HONEY: Honey in the wax combs, usually produced and sold as a separate unit, such as a wooden section 4-1/2" square, or a plastic round ring.

CONICAL ESCAPE: A cone-shaped bee escape which permits bees a one-way exit; used in a special escape board to free honey supers of bees.

CROSS-POLLINATION: The transfer of pollen from the anther of one flower to the stigma of another flower of the same species.

CREAMED HONEY: Honey that has been pasturized and undergone controlled granulation to produce a finely textured candied or crystalized honey which

spreads easily at room temperature.

CRYSTALIZE: See Granulate.

D

DEARTH: A period of time when there is no available forage for bees, due to weather conditions (rain, drought) or time of year.

DEXTROSE: Also known as glucose (grape sugar), it is a simple sugar (or monosaccharide) and is one of the two main sugars found in honey; forms most of the solid phase in granulated honey and its chemical formula is $C_2H_{12}O_6$.

DIATASE: A starch digesting enzyme in honey adversely affected by heat; used in some countries to test quality and heating history of stored honey.

DISEASE RESISTENCE: The ability of an organism to avoid a particular disease; primarily due to genetic immunity or avoidance behavior.

DIVISION: See Split.

DOUBLE STORY: Referring to a bee hive comprised of two deep supers, one for brood and one for honey.

DRIFTING: The movement of bees that have lost their location and enter other hives; common when hives are placed in long straight rows where returning foragers from the center hives tend to drift to the row ends.

DRONE: The male honey bee which comes from an unfertilized egg (and is therefore haploid) laid by a queen or less commonly, by a laying worker.

DRONE BROOD: Brood which matures into drones, reared in cells larger than worker brood.

DRONE CONGREGATING AREA (DCA): A specific area to which drones fly waiting for virgin queens to pass by; it is not known how or when they are formed, but drones return to the same spots year after year.

DRONE LAYERS: A drone laying queen

or laying workers.

DRONE LAYING QUEEN: A queen that can lay only unfertilized eggs, due to age, improper or no mating, disease or injury.

DYSENTERY: A condition in adult bees, seen in early spring, by the unusual amount of fecal discharge in or on the hive parts, or immediate vicinity of the hive; caused by unfavorable wintering conditions, low quality food (high moisture or impurities) or nosema infection.

E
EGGS: The first phase in the bee life cycle, usually laid by the queen, is the cylindrical egg 1/16in. (1.6mm) long; it is enclosed with a flexible shell or chorion.

ENTRANCE REDUCER: A notched wooden strip used to regulate the size of the bottom entrance.

ESCAPE BOARD: A board having one or more bee escapes in it; used to remove bees from supers.

EYELETS, METAL: A small metal piece fitting into the wire-holes of a frame's end bar; used to keep the reinforcing wires from cutting into the wood.

EXTRACTED HONEY: Honey removed from combs by means of a centrifugal extractor.

EXTRACTOR: A machine used to remove liquid honey from the combs, by means of centrifugal force; the combs remain intact.

F
FEEDERS: Various types of appliances for feeding bees artificially.

FERMENTING HONEY: Honey which contains too much water (greater than 20%) in which a chemical breakdown of the sugars takes place producing carbon dioxide and alcohol; caused by naturally-occurring osmophylic yeasts of the genus *Saccharomyces* (formerly *Zygosaccharomyces*).

FERTILIZED: Usually refers to eggs laid by a queen bee, they are fertilized with

sperm stored in the queen's spermatheca, in the process of being laid.

FESTOONING: The activity of young bees, engorged with honey, hanging on to each other and secreting beeswax.

FIELD BEES: Worker bees which are usually 21 or more days old and work outside to collect nectar, pollen, water and propolis; also called foragers.

FLIGHT PATH: Usually refers to the direction bees fly leaving their colony; if obstructed, may cause bees to become aggravated.

FORAGE: Natural food source of bees (nectar and pollen) from wild and cultivated flowers.

FOREIGN MATTER: In honey, unusually high amounts of wax, bee bodies, pollen grains, or other objectionable debris.

FOUNDATION, WAX: Thin sheets of beeswax embossed or stamped with the base of a worker (or rarely drone) cells on which bees will construct a complete comb (called drawn comb); also referred to as comb foundation, it comes wired or unwired.

FOUNDATION, WIRED: Comb foundation which includes evenly-spaced vertical wires for added support; used in brood or extracting frames.

FOUNDATION, UNWIRED: Comb foundation without vertical wires, used for cut comb or chunk (unextracted) honey.

FOULBROOD, AMERICAN: A malignant, contagious bacterial disease affecting bee larvae caused by a spore-forming bacteria *Bacillus larvae*.

FOULBROOD, EUROPEAN: A serious, infectious larval disease of honey bees caused by *Melissococcus pluton* (formerly *Streptococcus pluton*), a spore-forming bacteria.

FRAME: Four pieces of wood forming a rectangle, designed to hold honey comb, consisting of a top bar, two end bars, and a bottom bar (one or two pieces); usually spaced a bee-space apart in the super.

FRUCTOSE: See Levulose.

FUME BOARD: A device used to hold a set amount of a volatile chemical (a bee repellent like Bee Go) to drive bees from supers.

FUMAGILLIN: Bicyclohexyl-ammonium fumagillin, whose trade name is Fumidil-B (Abbot Labs), is a whitish soluble antibiotic powder discovered in 1952; it is mixed with sugar syrup and fed to bees to control Nosema disease.

G
GLOVES: Leather, cloth or rubber gloves worn while inspecting bees.

GLUCOSE: See Dextrose.

GLUCONIC ACID: See Acidity.

GRANULATE: The process by which honey, a super-saturated solution (more solids than liquid) will become solid or crystallize; speed of granulation depends on the kinds of sugars in the honey.

GUARD BEES: Worker bees about three weeks old, which have their maximum amount of alarm pheromone and venom; they challenge all incoming bees and other intruders.

GUM: A hollow log beehive, sometime called a log-gum (Appalachia), made by cutting out that portion of a tree containing bees and moving it to the apiary; since it contains no moveable frames, it is therefore illegal.

H
HAY FEVER: An allergic condition that afflicts many people; caused by various plant particles, airborne fungal spores or pollen.

HIVE: A manmade home for bees including a bottom board, hive bodies, frames enclosing honey combs, and covers.

HIVE BODY: A wooden box containing frames.

HIVE TOOL: A flat metal device with a curved scraping surface at one end and a flat blade at the other; used to open hives, pry apart and scrape frames.

HIVE STAND: A structure serving as a base support for a bee hive; it helps in extending the life of the bottom board by keeping it off damp ground.

HIVE STAPLES: Large C-shaped metal nails, hammered into the wooden hive parts to secure bottom to supers, and supers to super before moving a colony.

HOFFMAN SELF-SPACING FRAME: Frames that have the end bars wider at the top than the bottom to provide the proper spacing when frames are placed in the hive.

HONEYDEW: An excreted material from insects in the order *Homoptera* (aphids) which feed on plant sap; since it contains almost 90% sugar, it is collected by bees and stored as honeydew honey.

HONEY BEE: The common name for *Apis mellifera* (Honey bearer), a highly social insect, Order Hymenoptera (membranous wings); correctly printed as two words.

HONEY COLOR: Measured by a Pfund grader, honey colors are classified between water white to white, to amber to dark amber (7 gradations).

HONEY FLOW: A time when enough nectar-bearing plants are blooming such that bees can store a surplus of honey.

HONEY GATE: A faucet used for removing honey from tanks and other storage receptacles.

HONEY HOUSE: A building used for activities such as honey extraction, packaging and storage.

HONEY SAC: Also called honey stomach, an enlargement at the posterior (back) end of a bees' esophagus but lying in the front part of the abdomen, capable of expanding when full of liquid such as nectar or water.

HONEY SUPERS: Refers to hive bodies

used for honey production.

HONEY PLANTS: Plants whose flower (or other parts) yield enough nectar to produce a surplus of honey; examples are asters, basswood, citrus, eucalyptus, goldenrod and tupelo.

HORNETS and YELLOW JACKETS: Social insects belonging to the family *Vespidae*. Nest in paper or foliage material, with only an overwintering queen. Fairly aggressive, and carniverous, but generally beneficial, they can be a nuisance to man. Hornets and Yellow Jackets are often confused with Wasps and Honey Bees. Wasps are related to Hornets and Yellow Jackets, the most common of which are the paper wasps which nest in small exposed paper combs, suspended by a single support. Hornets, Yellow Jackets and Wasps are easy to distinguish by their larger size, shiny hairless body, and aggressiveness. Honey Bees are generally smaller, fuzzy brown or tan, and basically docile in nature.

HYPERSENSITIVE: A condition in which reactions to any environmental stimulus is life-threatening; such as honey bee venom.

I
IMPERFECT: Not fully formed, such as a worker, considered an imperfect female.

INCREASE: See Split.

INFERTILE: Incapable of producing a fertilized egg, as a laying worker.

INHIBINE: Antibacterial effect of honey caused by an accumulation of hydrogen peroxide, a result of the chemistry of honey.

INJECTIONS, DESENSITIZING: A series of injections given to persons with allergies, such as bee venom, so they might build up an immunity.

INNER COVER: An insulating cover fitting on top of the top super but underneath the outer cover, with an oblong hole in the center.

INSECTICIDE: Any chemical that kills insects.

INSPECTORS, STATE: Persons usually employed by state agriculture departments to inspect colonies of bees for diseases and pests.

INVERTASE: An enzyme in honey which splits the sucrose sugar molecule (a disaccharide) into its two components dextrose and levulose (monosaccharides).

ISOMERASE: A bacterial enzyme used to convert glucose in corn syrup into fructose, which is a sweeter sugar; called isomerose, is now used as a bee feed.

ITALIAN BEES: A common race of bees, *Apis mellifera ligustica,* with brown and yellow bands, from Italy; usually gentle and productive, but tend to rob.

L
LANGSTROTH, L. L.: A Philadelphia native and minister (1810-95), he lived for a time in Ohio where he continued his studies and writings of bees; recognized the importance of the bee space, resulting in the development of the movable-frame hive.

LARVA, CAPPED (pl -AE): The second developmental stage of a bee, ready to pupate or spin its cocoon (about the 10th day from the egg).

LAYING WORKERS: Worker bees which lay eggs in a colony hopelessly queenless; such eggs are infertile, since the workers cannot mate, and therefore become drones.

LEG BASKETS: Also called pollen baskets, a flattened depression surrounded by curved spines located on the outside of the tibiae of the bees' hind legs and adapted for carrying flower pollen or other dusts.

LEVULOSE: Also called fructose (fruit sugar), a monosaccharide commonly found in honey that is slow to granulate (such as *Robinia* or locust honey); chemical formula is also $C_6H_{12}O_6$, like glucose, but has it's carbonyl group (C=O) in a different place.

M

MANDIBLES: The jaws of an insect; used by bees to form the honey comb and scrape pollen, in fighting and picking up hive debris.

MATERNAL: From the mother's side of the family.

MIDNIGHT HYBRID: A combination of the Caucasian and Carniolan races.

MIGRATORY COVER: An outer cover used without an inner cover, that does not telescope over the sides of the hive; used by commercial beekeepers who frequently move hives.

MOISTURE CONTENT: In honey, the percentage of water should be no more than 18.6; any percentage higher than that will allow honey to ferment.

MOVABLE FRAMES: A frame constructed in such a way to preserve the bee space, so they can be easily removed; when in place, it remains unattached to its surroundings.

MOVING BOARD: A framed screen that fits over the top as a hive cover; used to move bees in hot weather to provide sufficient ventilation to keep bees from suffocating.

N

NATURAL HONEY: Unfiltered and unheated honey.

NECTAR: A liquid rich in sugars, manufactured by plants and secreted by nectary glands in or near flowers; the raw material for honey.

NECTARY GLANDS: Special nectar secreting glands usually found in flowers, whose function is to attract pollinating insects, such as honey bees for the purpose of cross pollination, by offering a carbohydrate-rich food.

NEWSPAPER METHOD: A technique to join together two strange colonies by providing a temporary newspaper barrier.

NOSEMA DISEASE: A widespread adult bee disease caused by a one-celled spore forming organism *Nosema apis*; it infects the gut lining.

NUC, NUCLEUS: A small colony of bees often used in queen rearing.

O

OSMOTIC PRESSURE: The minimum pressure that must be applied to a solution to prevent it from gaining water when it is separated from pure water by a permeable membrane; in honey, its ability to absorb water from the air or other microscopic organisms, about 2000 milliosmols/kg.

OUTER COVER: The last cover that fits over a hive to protect it from rain; the two most common kinds are telescoping and migratory covers.

OUTYARD: Also called out apiary, it is an apiary kept at some distance from the home or main apiary of a beekeeper; usually over a mile away from the home yard.

OVARY: The egg producing part of a plant or animal.

OVULE: An immature female germ cell which develops into a seed.

OXYTETRACYCLINE: An antibiotic sold under the trade name Terramycin; used to control American and European foulbrood diseases.

P

PACKAGE: See Shipping Cage.

PARTHENOGENESIS: The development of young from unfertilized eggs laid by virgin females (queen or worker); in bees, such eggs develop into drones.

PDB (PARADICHLOROBENZENE): A white crystalline substance whose vapors are heavier than air and are used to fumigate wax moths in combs.

PLAY FLIGHTS: Short flights taken in front and in the vicinity of the hive by young bees to acquaint them with hive location; sometimes mistaken for robbing or swarming preparations.

POISON SAC: Large oval sac containing venom and attached to the anterior (front) part of the sting; stores venom produced by the poison gland, and its primary ingredients are peptide and mellitin.

POLLEN: The dust-like male reproductive cells (gametophytes) of flowers, formed in the anthers, and important as a protein source for bees; pollen is essential for bees to rear brood.

POLLEN BASKET: See Leg Basket.

POLLEN PELLETS: The cakes of pollen packed in the leg baskets of bees and transported back to the colony.

POLLEN SUBSTITUTE: A food material which is used to substitute wholly for pollen in the bees' diet; usually contains all or part of soy flour, brewers' yeast, wheast, powdered sugar, or other ingredients.

POLLEN TRAP: A device for collecting the pollen pellets from the hind legs of worker bees; usually forces the bees to squeeze through a screen mesh which scrapes off the pellets.

POLLEN TUBE: A slender thread-like growth, containing sperm cells, which penetrates the female tissue (stigma) of a flower until it eventually reaches the ovary; there the sperm cells unite with the ovule.

POLLINATION: The transfer of pollen from the anthers to the stigma of flowers.

PORTER BEE ESCAPE: Introduced in 1891, the escape is a device that allows the bees a one-way exit between two thin and pliable metal bars that yield to the bees' push; used to free honey supers of bees but may clog since drone bees often get stuck.

PROPOLIS: Plant resins collected and modified by bees; used to fill in small spaces inside the hive.

PROPOLIZE: To fill with propolis, or bee glue; used to strengthen the comb and seal cracks, it also has antimicrobial properties.

PROTEIN: Naturally occurring complex organic substances, such as pollen; composed of amino acids, the building blocks of protein, containing the group -NH_2.

PUPA (pl-AE): The third stage in the development of the bee during which it is inactive and sealed in its cocoon; the organs of the larva are replaced by those which will be used as an adult.

Q

QUEEN: A fully developed mated female bee responsible for all the egg laying of a colony; recognized by other bees by her special pheromones (odors).

QUEEN CAGE: A special cage in which queens are shipped and/or introduced to a colony, usually with 5 or 6 young workers, called attendants, and a candy plug.

QUEEN CELL: A special elongated cell resembling a peanut shell in which the queen is reared; usually over an inch in length, it hangs vertically from the comb.

QUEEN CUP: A cup-shaped cell hanging vertically from the comb, but containing no egg; also made artificially of wax or plastic to raise queens.

QUEEN EXCLUDER: A device made of wire, wood or zinc (or any combination thereof) having openings of .163 to .164 inch, which permits workers to pass but excludes queens and drones; used to confine the queen to a specific part of the hive, usually the brood nest.

QUEENRIGHT: A colony that contains a laying queen.

R

RACES OF BEES: The four most common races of *Apis* are *mellifera, cerana, dorsata* and *florea*; other newly discovered races are currently under investigation.

RADIAL EXTRACTOR: A centrifugal force machine to throw out honey but leave the combs intact; the frames are placed like spokes of a wheel, top bars towards the wall, to take advantage of the upward slope of the cells.

RAW HONEY: See Natural Honey.

REQUEEN: To introduce a new queen into a queenless hive.

REVERSING: The act of exchanging places of different hive bodies of the same colony; usually for the purpose of nest expansion, the super full of brood and the queen is placed below an empty super to allow the queen extra laying space.

ROBBING: The act of bees stealing honey/nectar from other colonies; also applied to bees cleaning out wet supers or cappings left uncovered by beekeepers.

ROPY CHARACTERISTIC: A diagnostic test for American foulbrood in which the decayed larvae form an elastic rope when drawn out with a toothpick.

ROUND SECTIONS: Sections of comb honey in plastic round rings instead of square wooden boxes.

ROYAL JELLY: A highly nutritious, milky white glandular secretion of young (nurse) bees; used to feed the queen and young larvae.

S
SACBROOD: A brood disease of bees caused by a filterable virus which interferes with the molting process; the dead larva resemble a bag of fluid.

SCREENED VENTILATED BOARD: A framed screen used to cover the top of a hive being moved in hot weather.

SECTIONS: Small wooden (or plastic) boxes used to produce comb honey.

SELF-POLLINATION: The act of a single flower, or flower from the same plant, pollinating itself.

SELF-STERILE: The inability of a flower, such as a fruit tree, to be fertilized within its own variety; it is only fertilized by pollen from another variety.

SETTLING TANK: A large capacity container used to settle extracted honey; air bubbles and debris will float to the top,

clarifying the honey.

SKEP: A beehive without moveable frames, usually made of twisted straw in the form of a basket; it's use is illegal in the U.S.

SLUMGUM: The refuse from melted combs and cappings after the wax has been rendered or removed; usually contains cocoons, pollen, bee bodies and dirt.

SMOKER: A metal container with attached bellows which burns organic fuels to generate smoke; used to control aggressive behavior of bees during colony inspections.

SOLAR WAX MELTER OR EXTRACTOR: A glass-covered insulated box used to melt wax from combs and cappings using the heat of the sun.

SPERM CELLS: The male reproductive cells (gametes) which fertilize eggs; also called spermatozoa.

SPERMATHECA: A small sac connected with the oviduct (vagina) of the queen bee in which is stored the spermatozoa received in mating with drones.

SPLIT: To divide a colony for the purpose of increasing the number of hives.

STARLINE HYBRID: An Italian bee hybrid known for vigor and honey production.

STIGMA: Receptive portion of the female part of a flower to which pollen adheres.

STING: An organ belonging exclusively to female insects developed from egg laying mechanisms, used to defend the colony; modified into a piercing shaft through which venom is injected.

STING SAC: See Poison Sac.

STRAINING SCREEN: A metal or plastic screen through which honey is filtered; also serves as a base for other, finer screening material.

SUGAR SYRUP: Feed for bees, containing sucrose or table (cane) sugar and hot water in various ratios.

SUPER: A receptacle in which bees store honey; usually placed over or above the brood nest; so called brood supers contain brood.

SUPERING: The act of placing honey supers on a colony in expectation of a honey flow.

SUPERSEDURE: Rearing a new queen to replace the mother queen in the same hive; shortly after the daughter queen begins to lay eggs, the mother queen disappears.

SURPLUS HONEY: Any extra honey removed by the beekeeper, over and above what the bees require for their own use, such as winter food stores.

SWARM: A collection of bees, containing at least one queen, that split apart from the mother colony to establish a new one; a natural method of propagation of honey bees.

SWARMING SEASON: The time of year, usually mid-summer, when swarms usually issue.

T
TERRAMYCIN: See Oxytetracycline.

THORAX: The central region of an insect to which the wings and legs are attached.

TOP BAR: The top part of a frame.

TRAVEL STAINS: The darkened appearance on the surface of honey comb caused by bees walking over its surface.

U
UNCAPPING KNIFE: A knife used to shave off the cappings of sealed honey prior to extraction; the knives can be heated by hot water, steam or electricity.

UNCAPPING TANK: A container over which frames of honey are uncapped; usually strains out the honey which is then collected.

UNFERTILIZED: An ovum or egg which

has not been united with the sperm.

V
VARROA JACOBSONI: An external mite parasite on honey bees.

VEIL: A protective netting that covers the face and neck; allows ventilation, easy movement and good vision.

VIRGIN QUEEN: An unmated queen bee.

W
WARMING CABINET: An insulated box or room heated to liquify honey.

WASP: A close relative of honey bees, usually in the family *Vespidae*; they are carniverous, some species preying on bees (see also, Hornet).

WAX: See Beeswax.

WAX GLANDS: The eight glands located on the last 4 visible, ventral abdominal segments of young worker bees; they secrete beeswax droplets.

WAX MOTH: Usually refers to the Greater wax moth, *Galleria mellonella* whose larvae bore through and destroy honey comb as they eat out its impurities.

WAX SCALE: A drop of liquid beeswax which hardens into a scale upon contact with air; in this form it is shaped into comb.

WAX TUBE FASTENER: A metal tube for applying a fine stream of melted wax to secure a sheet of foundation to an ungrooved frame.

WIND-POLLINATED: Plants whose flowers manufacture light pollen (and usually no nectar) which is released into the air to fall by chance on a receptive stigma; examples include the grasses (corn, oats) and conifers (pines).

WINDBREAKS: Specially constructed, or naturally occurring barriers to reduce the force of the (winter) winds on a beehive.

WINTER CLUSTER: A tight ball of bees within the hive to generate heat; forms when outside temperature falls below

57°F (14°C).

WINTER HARDINESS: The ability of some strains of honey bees to survive long winters by frugal use of stored honey.

WIRE, FRAME: Thin 28# wire used to reinforce foundation destined for the broodnest or honey extractor.

WIRE CONE ESCAPE: A one-way cone formed by window screen mesh used to direct bees from a house or tree into a temporary hive.

WORKER BEES: Infertile female bees whose reproductive organs are only partially developed, responsible for carrying out all the routine work of the colony.

Reference Books Available From The A.I. Root Library

ABC & XYZ of Bee Culture
The A.I. Root Co., Medina, OH

Honey Bee Pests, Predators & Diseases, Third Edition
Edited by Roger Morse & Kim Flottum

Selling Honey
Best of Bee Culture Series

Colony Record Book
A.I. Root Co.

For Details Write:
The A.I. Root Co.
623 W. Liberty St.
Medina, OH 44256

Index

A

Acarapis woodi 109
advertising 100
Africanized Honey Bees 110
ants 113
apiary locations, choosing 18
Apis Cerana 109
Apistan® 111
associations
    beekeeping 120
    benefits of belonging 121
    forming a new 120

B

balling the queen 67
basic beekeeping equipment 1
bee bread 52
bee suit 13
bee space 8
bee trees, removing bees from 77
beehive, parts of 8
bees, arriving dead 5
bees, hybrids 7
beeswax 61
    how bees make 39, 61
    melting 61
    preparing for sale 61
bottling honey 92
bottom board, using 10

C

candy plug, in queen cage 4
canning with honey 97
Chalkbrood 104
colony organization 32
comb and cut comb honey
    harvesting 57
    packaging 58
    problems with 46
    producing 44, 45, 58, 59, 60
    sections 44
    selling 93
combs, rendering old 62
containers 43
cooking with honey 97
cotyledons 51
covers
    inner 5
    migratory 10
creamed honey, Dyce method 93

D

Demeree method, swarm control 69
diseases, adult 106

diseases, brood (right column)

diseases, brood 102
dividing colonies, how to 73
drifting 79
    avoiding 3
drone, layers 79
    role of 35
dysentery 86

E

Endosperm 51
entrance, top 85
equalizing colonies
    with booster packages 81
    newspaper method 81
    removing brood 81
escape board 14
ether roll testing method 111
excluders, queen 14, 43
extracted honey
    equipment for producing 42
    packaging 92
    settling 89
extraction, tools for 54
    basket extractor 55
    radial extractor 55
eyelets, metal 11

F

feeding
    equipment for 5
    colonies 28
    dry sugar 82
    fall 82
    packages 5
    spring 87
fermentation 89
filtering honey 89
fondant candy 82
Foulbrood
    American 102
    European 104
    signs of 6
foundation 11
frames
    construction 10
    Hoffman, self-spacing 10
    movable 10

G

gates, honey 43
getting bees 15
gloves 13
grading honey 94
granulation 89

grease patties 109

H

harvesting honey
    how to 54
    tools for 54
hay fever 50
heating honey 90
high fructose corn syrup 82
hive body, sizes 42
hive stand 9
hive tool, using 14
honey
    color 94
    as a food 95
    fermentation 89
    filtering 89
    nutrition properties of 95
    raw / organic 93
    re-liquefying 90
    settling 57
    storing 89
    straining 57
honey flow
    what is 41
    spring and summer 41
hybrid bees 7

I

inspections, packages 6
inspectors 15
IPM mite strategies 113

K

knives, uncapping 55

L

larvae, capped 6
laying workers 79
legal problems with bees 117

M

marketing honey 98
menthol crystals 109
mice, problems with 114
mites, as pests of bees 109
moving bees 6

N

news release, writing 123
newspaper method 80
Nosema disease 106

O

ordinances for bees 117
organizing a bee assn. 120
ovules 81

P

packages
    examining 23
    hiving 3
    ordering 15

packing for winter 84
phorsey 111
pollen
    as a food 52
    packaging 64
    trapping 63
    what is 50
pollination 48
protection 13

Q

queen
    cage, in package 3
    balling 67
    finding 25
    introducing a new 66
    laying season 33
    loss of, signs 34
    raising a new 34
    requeening 66
    role of, in colony 33
    supercedure 66

R

races of honey bees 7
    Apis mellifera carnica 7
    Apis mellifera caucasica 7
    Apis mellifera ligustica 7
record keeping 65
residential areas, bees in 115
reversing supers 31
robbing 76
round sections 57

S

sacbrood 105
skeps 8
smokers
    using 12
    lighting 21
sticky board 111
stings, avoiding 13, 22
sugar syrup 82
supers, warming 54
swarming 68
    artificial 73
    capturing with clipped queen 69
    capturing with unclipped queen 71
    capturing 71
    controlling 69
    indications of 69
    prevention 72

T

tanks
    storage 57
    uncapping 55
Tracheal mites 109
Terra patties 109

U
uncapping tools 55
V
Varroa jacobsoni 109
veil 13
W
water for bees 18
wax moth
   control 108

life cycle 106
wind breaks 83
wintering
   problems 85
   dysentery & nosema 86
   in the north 83
   in the south 83
workers
   function & duties 36
   laying 79

Notes